NEAR ZERO

Born in Glasgow, Scotland, in 1920, DAVID KEITH CHALMERS MACDONALD received his M.A. in mathematics and natural philosophy from Edinburgh University in 1941, and his Ph.D. in 1946 after serving with the Royal Mechanical and Electrical Engineers during World War II. He then went to Oxford as a research fellow. There he continued his graduate studies and took a second Ph.D. (1949).

In 1951 Dr. MacDonald went to Canada to start a laboratory in low temperature and solid state physics for the National Research Council in Ottawa. This laboratory has become one of the finest and most productive of its kind in the world, and has grown from a staff of one —himself—to a group of fifteen scientists.

Dr. MacDonald has contributed significantly to our knowledge of the transport properties of metals and alloys. Some of his most important contributions have been in the field of electrical resistance at low temperatures. Furthermore, under his guidance the Low Temperature Group has done valuable work on specific heats, atomic spacings in crystals, and semiconductor physics.

In 1955 Dr. MacDonald was appointed honorary chairman of the Physics Department at Ottawa University. He has helped to launch this department on a program of low temperature physics research. Through his many radio and television broadcasts, he has also brought science to wider audiences and has thereby increased Canadian interest in physics.

Dr. MacDonald was elected a Fellow of the Royal Society of Edinburgh in 1954, a Fellow of the Royal Society of Canada in 1958, and a Fellow of the Royal Society of London in 1960. In 1960 the Canadian Association of Physicists awarded him its fifth Gold Medal for Achievement in Physics. He is a frequent contributor to scientific journals.

NEAR ZERO

An Introduction to Low Temperature Physics

D. K. C. MacDONALD

Published by Anchor Books
Doubleday & Company, Inc.
Garden City, New York
1961

ILLUSTRATIONS BY ROBERT L. KELLEY
TYPOGRAPHY BY SUSAN SIEN

Library of Congress Catalog Card Number 61–16716
Copyright © 1961 by Educational Services Incorporated
Printed in the United States of America
First Edition

THE SCIENCE STUDY SERIES

The Science Study Series offers to students and to the general public the writing of distinguished authors on the most stirring and fundamental topics of science, from the smallest known particles to the whole universe. Some of the books tell of the role of science in the world of man, his technology and civilization. Others are biographical in nature, telling the fascinating stories of the great discoverers and their discoveries. All the authors have been selected both for expertness in the fields they discuss and for ability to communicate their special knowledge and their own views in an interesting way. The primary purpose of these books is to provide a survey within the grasp of the young student or the layman. Many of the books, it is hoped, will encourage the reader to make his own investigations of natural phenomena.

The Series, which now offers topics in all the sciences and their applications, had its beginning in a project to revise the secondary schools' physics curriculum. At the Massachusetts Institute of Technology during 1956 a group of physicists, high school teachers, journalists, apparatus designers, film producers, and other specialists organized the Physical Science Study Committee, now operating as a part of Educational Services Incorporated, Watertown, Massachusetts. They pooled their knowledge and experience toward the design and creation of aids to the learning of physics. Initially their effort was supported by the National Science Foundation, which has continued to aid the program. The Ford Foundation, the Fund for the Advancement of Education, and the Alfred P. Sloan Foundation have also given support. The Committee has created a textbook, an extensive film series, a laboratory guide, especially designed apparatus, and a teachers' source book.

The Series is guided by a Board of Editors, consisting of Bruce F. Kingsbury, Managing Editor; John H. Durston, General Editor; Paul F. Brandwein, the Conservation Foundation and Harcourt, Brace and Company; Francis L. Friedman, Massachusetts Institute of Technology; Samuel A. Goudsmit, Brookhaven National Laboratory; Philippe LeCorbeiller, Harvard University; Gerard Piel, *Scientific American;* and Herbert S. Zim, Simon and Schuster, Inc.

PREFACE

This little book makes no pretense whatsoever to be a comprehensive survey of all the topics that are interesting in low temperature physics. I have tended to concentrate on those parts that I thought I knew something about and for a very good reason. It is hard enough to write when you know what you are talking about, but it seems to me well nigh impossible when you do not!

There are quite a lot of footnotes in this book, but they are meant to help by explaining some terms which may not always be familiar, or to tell a little about the most outstanding scientists we meet in this field. But if footnotes distract you, just ignore them, at least on a first reading. But perhaps I am an optimist if I imagine the book will be worth a second reading!

I have one suggestion to make. This book is quite small, but for those who cannot spare the time to read it all, I suggest that perhaps the first and last chapters (which could be read in the reverse order, if you like) might give some idea of the fascination which the author, at any rate, has found in the subject.

I should like to thank:

Dr. J. G. Daunt, Dr. K. Mendelssohn, and the Royal Society in connection with Fig. 12 which was suggested by a figure in a paper by Drs. Daunt and Mendelssohn (Proc. Royal Society *A 942, 423,* 1939).

Dr. D. Shoenberg and the Cambridge University Press. Fig. 10 was redrawn from Table VIII of Dr. Shoenberg's book *Superconductivity* (Cambridge University Press, 1952).

Sir Lawrence Bragg, Director, The Royal Institution, for his kindness in supplying the photograph from which Plate V was reproduced.

Dr. Howard O. McMahon, senior vice-president, Arthur D. Little Inc., Cambridge, Massachusetts, who very kindly supplied a photograph from which Plate VI was reproduced.

Miss P. Fairfield for her able assistance in typing numerous drafts of the manuscript; Miss J. Spong, and my wife and my daughter, Aileen, for help in checking the manuscript, reading proofs, etc.

Ottawa: 1961   D. K. C. MacDonald

CONTENTS

NEAR ZERO

CHAPTER 1

WHAT IS LOW TEMPERATURE PHYSICS?

In the North American winter it is not too rare for nighttime temperatures to fall to around −40°F (which happens to be the same as −40°C). Maybe it is difficult for most people who have to live through these winters to understand why anyone in a laboratory would deliberately produce temperatures as cold as this and, indeed, far far colder. And, they might well ask also, what use would it be? In this book I hope to show you why experiments at very low temperatures can help greatly in understanding the behavior of the world around us—even at normal temperatures—and in helping man to make better use of nature, by improving conductors for transmitting electricity, for example. But I should like to say that in any case I believe any systematic investigation of the behavior of nature, be it at high or low temperature, at the North Pole or in the Sahara Desert, or of the animate or inanimate world, is worth doing *for its own sake*. I believe that one of the most important traits that distinguish humankind from other animals is this capacity for continuous inquiry. Some men have always maintained a keen sense of wonder in trying to fathom what goes on in nature.

Now do not mistake me. I am not advocating particularly what is sometimes called "the ivory-

tower scientist" who is supposed to be quite isolated from the rest of the world. I myself am very
glad that an understanding of science has, in fact, led
to such pleasant results as record players (since I
happen to enjoy music), has given us moving pic-
tures, electric stoves and refrigerators (since I enjoy
eating and drinking), spring mattresses, oil furnaces
for heating houses (since I certainly like comfort,
when I can get it) and a host of other things. That
does not mean, on the other hand, that I am not disturbed and unhappy, as we all should be, about
the prospects for self-destruction which society has
prompted technology to produce from the discoveries
of science. The results of scientific research are in
themselves neither good nor evil; it is what man
chooses to do with them which decides. But, having
said this, I still want to emphasize that I believe that
scientific inquiry or "research" is in itself a worthwhile
and thoroughly *human* (or humane, if you prefer)
thing to do. I do not believe it has to have any
"angles" to it. It *may* have, of course. A man may be
anxious for some sort of fame, to make a better salary
or something of the kind, and such ambition just re-
flects the fact that scientists and scholars are human
beings like the rest of us, but I think it is sad how
often people today expect to find some ulterior mo-
tive or hidden purpose for what everyone is doing in
life. I believe there is little doubt that the finest and
most worthwhile research is carried out by men who
are—for the time, at any rate—quite uninterested in
anything but the question itself they are trying to
solve. The whole business, of course, is really very
similar to the urge that drives men like Hillary and
Tensing to make the enormous effort to climb Mount
Everest. Again, do not mistake me, every man to his
own taste! I myself would be appalled at the thought

of setting out to climb even a very small mountain, and I am sure Mount Everest would freeze the very marrow in my bones, but then maybe to Sir Edmund Hillary the thought of doing experiments at very low temperatures would be a most unwelcome cup of tea. So back to the business in hand.

I should like first to try to give you some over-all picture of what we mean by low temperatures and their general significance in physical science, and then in later chapters go on to discuss things in more detail. So you must forgive me if much of what I say here is not too precise. If I succeed in giving you a rough picture of what we are about, I shall be glad.

The temperature of the sun on its surface is about 6000°C, but that is not where the real business goes on that produces all the heat which the sun radiates into space. Down in the interior, where nuclear reactions produce the energy to keep the sun going, the temperature is more like *forty million* degrees Centigrade—or so astrophysicists tell us.[1] This temperature is about a hundred thousand times as hot as the general temperature that *we* live at, and certainly there can be no doubt that the whole business of very hot nuclear reactions is a very important part of physical science. But what about things that are a hundred thousand times *colder* than the world around us? Is there any point or purpose in studying things as cold as this? And indeed what could we mean by things that are a hundred thousand times colder? These two questions are more or less at the heart of low temperature physics. I shall try to answer them, roughly and in turn.

[1] I have just seen recently that one expert, Professor Hermann Bondi, says that the temperature at the center of the sun is only a mere thirteen million degrees; there even seems to be quite a bit of uncertainty in that!

Heat, Motion, and Atomic Disorder

First there is the matter of the "hotness" of bodies. Up to about a hundred years ago there was still some doubt about just what went on in matter as it became hot, or, in other words, exactly what heat itself is. Of course, in a sense we all know perfectly well what we mean when we say that *we* are hot. In this usage hot generally means that we have a strong sense of discomfort; we may even feel quite nauseated if we get too hot, and from the medical point of view such a symptom is very important. We should never forget that all physical science starts originally from human sensation. For example, the idea of mass starts from the human appreciation that bodies are "heavy"; force is born from the human sensation of pushing hard on something to make it move, and so on. On the other hand, you cannot ask a chair and a table whether "they" are feeling uncomfortable, or whether they are too hot or too cold, and, furthermore, without some independent *scale* that we can use to measure these things we could never agree among ourselves about how hot or how cold things are. So we cannot rely on our own personal sensations alone to build up understanding of heat and cold in nature generally. It was Benjamin Thomson[2] (who later be-

[2] Benjamin Thomson was born in Woburn, Mass., U.S.A., in 1753, and played a major part in founding the Royal Institution in London, England, whose early directors were Sir Humphrey Davy and Michael Faraday. His famous paper published in the Philosophical Transactions of the Royal Society of London in 1798 dealing with the production of heat by friction, started with the introduction: "It frequently happens, that in the ordinary affairs and occupations of life, opportunities present themselves of contemplating some of the most curious operations of nature . . . and [I] am persuaded, that a habit of keeping the eyes open to everything

came Count Rumford of Bavaria) who seems to have been one of the first to state clearly and explicitly just what is meant physically when we say that something gets hotter. In 1798 he wrote: ". . . it appears to me to be extremely difficult, if not quite impossible, to form any distinct idea of anything capable of being excited, and communicated, in the manner the heat was excited, and communicated in these experiments, except it be MOTION [i.e., of the atoms]." That is to say, when we heat something up, the atoms of the body begin to vibrate more and more strongly, or, in other words, the atoms have more energy. Now let me make it clear that this definition does not alter in any way the fact of how *you* as a person feel when you are hot or cold, but it does mean that this increase of energy is a common property of all substances, whether living or inert, as they are heated, and this property is something we can *measure* and agree about. The part of science that is involved with the hotness or coldness of bodies (i.e., their temperature) is concerned basically with the energy that the atoms or molecules have.

Let us turn to a familiar situation and think about a lump of ice on an extremely cold day. If you examined the ice by means of suitable X-rays (which enable us to find out how the atoms or molecules are arranged), you would find that the water molecules are arrayed in a very regular pattern in space forming what we call a "lattice." It is this regular arrangement or pattern of atoms that gives many substances an obvious crystalline form, and it is because of this atomic pattern that snowflakes have the beautiful and

---

that is going on in the ordinary course of . . . life has oftener led . . . to useful doubts, and sensible schemes . . . than all the more intense meditations of philosophers, in the hours expressly set apart for study." *No comment!*

regular shapes one often sees. Now even on the coldest
day we experience on earth the molecules making up
the ice crystal will *not* be completely stationary. If
you could go down to their level of size with a "pair
of patent double million magnifying gas microscopes"
(Sam Weller, *Pickwick Papers*), you would see that
each molecule was jiggling about quite fast, but on
the average still staying in more or less the same position. Or, as one says more technically, the molecules
would be vibrating about a position of equilibrium
(Fig. 1). Now let us imagine that we heat up this
very cold piece of ice a bit and go on watching the
molecules; we should find that they jiggled about
more and more strongly as the temperature rose, and
this increasing movement of the molecules is simply
the heat energy that the crystal of ice has. There
would come a time as we went on heating the ice
(when we reached 0° Centigrade), when this jiggling
around would become so strong that the molecules
making up the ice crystal could no longer remain in a
nice regular pattern. When this happens—and it happens quite suddenly—every molecule can start moving
about among the others so that not only do they have
a fairly rapid jiggling movement, but they also start
to *diffuse* rapidly from place to place, not staying for
long in any one position. Now you might expect when
this happens that something quite dramatic would be
observed in the piece of ice. And certainly it is dramatic when you think of it; this hard brittle solid material known as ice suddenly turns into a wet runny
liquid, which we call water, and flows all over the
place. And in many ways this business of sudden
melting is still one of the most remarkable things in
nature. Without it we would miss some of the most
exciting sights around us, particularly in Canada,
where one sees the spring "breakup" of large rivers.

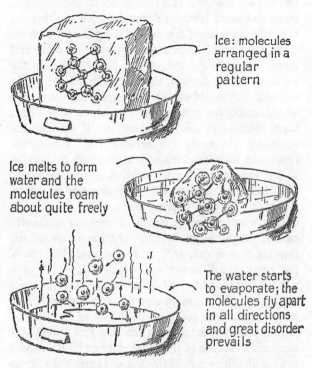

Ice: molecules arranged in a regular pattern

Ice melts to form water and the molecules roam about quite freely

The water starts to evaporate; the molecules fly apart in all directions and great disorder prevails

FIG. 1. *Atoms or molecules such as in this crystalline solid vibrate about an equilibrium position. However, as more and more energy is put into the solid, these vibrations become violent enough so that the atoms or molecules no longer have an equilibrium position, and we have in turn a liquid and then a gas.*

But let us go on a bit more. The ice is now melted into water. Suppose we continue to heat this water further; we shall find that the molecules move around more and more freely. (Technically we say that the viscosity diminishes; this sort of thing is very obvious if you heat up oil, which quickly becomes more and more "runny.") As long as we do not heat up the water *too* much though, the molecules on the whole will still stay together. The molecules actually have an attraction for one another, which is what keeps them together in the first place, but if we heat the water up too much (to around 100° Centigrade now), the individual molecules then will be moving so fast that they will start to break away completely from the crowd and fly off, perhaps never to return. When this starts to happen, we say that we are producing water vapor or steam. The water molecules have so much energy that they fly off in all directions, forming now a gas, and, as I have said, this gas is just what we call steam.

Now I should like to take a rather simple analogy to suggest, perhaps more directly, what the main features are that are going on here. Let us imagine we have a crowd of small boys who are first sitting in a classroom (maybe of the old-fashioned kind) in neat rows and columns at their desks. There is a schoolteacher in the room who can be very strict (dare I say he or she might even have the right to paddle someone?), and at first the boys are sitting at their desks being rather still and quiet and in very good order. But later the teacher's attention becomes somewhat distracted, and the boys start wriggling about in their desks more and more, until finally when the teacher has left the room for a few minutes the boys start running from one desk to another. When that happens we might say that the regular or "crystalline" pattern of boys had "melted," and we now have a fluid collection of boys. The boys still think for a while that the teacher is coming back, so on the whole they stay put in the classroom although still running from desk to desk. After a little while, however, they begin to realize that the teacher is not coming back at all, and rather soon they start running out through the doors of the classroom, and some of them even jump out the windows and rush to the playground, then into the fields, so getting farther and farther away from school and most unlikely to return (at least until tomorrow). Now I think we might say that the liquid state of schoolboys has "vaporized," and we have a "gas" of boys rushing off in all directions at high speeds, and on the whole paying very little attention to one another. What I want to bring out here is that as time went on with these boys, things got more and more *disordered*. In somewhat the same way when we heated up the block of ice until it ultimately vaporized, the motion of the atoms also got more and more irregular and *disordered,* until finally the atoms too flew off in all directions. Broadly speaking, the higher the temperature that any physical body has, the greater the amount of atomic disorder, and, conversely, if you cool things down to low temperatures, the cooling generally produces more and more atomic order in the system. We might complete the analogy—rather crudely—by suggesting that the schoolteacher is something like a low temperature physicist, who can introduce order into a situation where none existed before.

Let us take another example to get the general idea. If you connect a piece of metal wire such as copper or silver to a small electric battery (Fig. 2), an electric current will flow through it for some time, but ultimately the battery will get tired and no longer be able

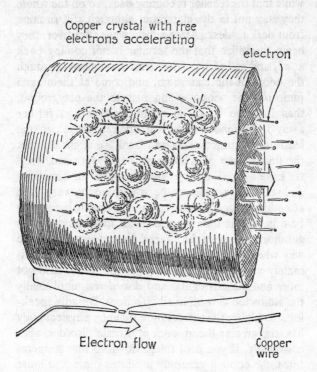

Copper crystal with free
electrons accelerating

electron

Electron flow   Copper
                                        wire

FIG. 2. *An orderly arrangement, the "face centered cubic" crystal of copper, is seen here with the aid of Sam Weller's magnifier. The free electrons bouncing and careening about are nevertheless progressing steadily to the right under the influence of the voltage applied between the ends of the wire.*

to drive the current through the wire. Now we know today that a piece of metal can conduct electricity because when the atoms arrange themselves in the crystal structure that composes the metal, each atom has given up one or two electrons to a common "fund," and this collection of electrons is more or less free to move through the metal if we want them to. When we apply an electric voltage to the metal, the voltage gives a shove to these electrons and starts a flow of electric current. If we keep shoving with the electric voltage, and nothing stops the electrons, they will go faster and faster, and you might think that we should have an electric current in the wire getting bigger and bigger all the time. But something else happens. As soon as the "cloud" of electrons starts to move through the metal, the electrons find it difficult to make their way past the very atoms that constitute the metal. The electrons are bumping into the atoms very frequently—they "collide" with the atoms, as we say. And this colliding has two effects. First, the continual bumping of the electrons into the surrounding atoms gives rise to electrical "friction" (what is technically called the electrical resistance of the metal), and the resistance limits the speed that the electrons go at; in other words, it limits the electric current that will flow under a given voltage. This proportionality of the electric current to the applied voltage is known as Ohm's Law.[3] Secondly, pushing the electrons

[3] Georg Simon Ohm (1787–1854). Ohm was a German physicist who was a Professor at Munich from 1852. The universal unit of electrical resistance is called the ohm in his honor. A resistance of one ohm allows a current of one ampere to pass when an electric force of one volt is applied. Perhaps we should mention here that the ampere is named after the famous French physicist and mathematician André Marie Ampère (1775–1836), who made fundamental studies of electricity and magnetism. The volt is named in honor of Alessandro Volta (1745–1827), who invented the voltaic

through the metal uses up energy, and so the battery
after some time gets worn out; the electrical energy
that it originally had has been used up in overcoming
the electrical resistance of the metal. Now if the
atoms are vibrating or jiggling about strongly, then
the electrons will find it very difficult to get through,
and the resistance of the metal should be high. Conversely, if we can cut down the vibration of the atoms
to a small value, it should be much easier for the
electrons to find their way through, and so the resistance should diminish. But we saw earlier that the
vibrations of the atoms should progressively increase
as the temperature goes up, and we should therefore
expect that the electrical resistance of the metal *also*
should increase if we heat it up, and conversely the
electrical resistance should diminish if we cool the
metal down.

Indeed, this is just what we find. Suppose, for example, we take a pure piece of copper wire. Its resistance at room temperature might be one ohm; that
is to say, a one-volt battery will drive a current of
one ampere through the wire. If now we heat that
copper wire, in a flame, up to a dull red heat so that
its temperature is about 600°C, we should find that
its resistance had risen to about three ohms. So we
would need a *three*-volt battery to make one ampere
of current flow now; because the metal is very hot,
the atoms are vibrating so strongly that the electrons
need three times as much force to push them through
at the same rate. But if we take the same piece of
wire and, instead of heating it up, we put it into some
liquid air (whose temperature is around –190°C), we
find that its resistance has now *dropped* to about one-
fifth of an ohm; if we put our one-volt battery on it,

pile which was effectively the first electric battery providing
electricity from a chemical reaction.

we would get five amperes of current flowing. Liquid air is very cold stuff, and, since the atoms of the metal are now vibrating much less vigorously than they were at room temperature, the electrons can make their way through much more easily. If we go further and put the wire in some liquid helium, which is colder still, the resistance might well go down to as little as perhaps one thousandth of an ohm; it would need only a thousandth of a volt to make the one-ampere current flow. At this very low temperature (liquid helium is about one hundred times colder than room temperature) the heat vibrations of the atoms are so very weak that they have very little effect in stopping the passage of the electrons.

The situation is perhaps a little like a cocktail party. If the party goes well, then, after an hour, say, the guests may become so animated that you will find it very difficult to get across from one side of the room to the other without bumping into people. On the other hand, if the "ice" never gets broken (the dread of every hostess), people may become so "cold" and withdrawn that they will stand around without saying a word, and you will have no difficulty in crossing the room at any time.

We can sum up the general situation: When you heat things (that is, raise them to a high temperature), the arrangement of the atoms becomes more and more disordered, while if you cool them down sufficiently, you will increase the atomic order. It follows readily from this that low temperature physics enables one to measure things with greater and greater precision, because the atomic order lets us "see" more and more of the details standing out—roughly speaking, we see more just because things are not jiggling about so much. It is rather like the difference between looking out your window at a large tree (as I am do-

ing at this moment) trying to make out the details of
the leaves on an absolutely calm summer's day and,
on the other hand, watching the same tree when there
is half a gale blowing. When everything is waving
about madly in the gale, you still know it is a tree all
right, but you could not tell much about the shape of
the leaves and so on, even if you tried to look at the
tree through a telescope. But when the weather is
calm and the tree quite still, as it is at this minute, I
can see that each leaf has just five points. Moreover, if
I cared to use a telescope, I could certainly pick out
the veins and other details of the leaves. Thus the
more still and ordered things are, the better one can
see fine detail. So by using very low temperatures to
increase the order among the atoms, the physicist can
better examine the fine detail in matter. By the way, a
physicist named Clausius[4] coined a special word for
the amount of disorder in physical systems—it is called
entropy.

One of the most important laws of physics (or indeed of all science) says that if nature is left to operate by itself, entropy as a whole always tends to increase (this is one form of the Second Law of
Thermodynamics). What *that* means, roughly speaking, is that if you leave things to themselves they tend
on the whole to get more and more jumbled. If any
housewife, and particularly the mother of small children, should happen to read this, I am sure she will
feel that she knows exactly what I mean. She says: "I
spend all day trying to put the house into some kind
of order, and as soon as I turn my back the place
just seems to mess itself up before I know where I

---

[4] Rudolf Julius Emanuel Clausius (1822–1888). He was
a Professor at the famous Federal University (E.T.H.) at
Zürich in Switzerland from 1855 to 1867, and later at the
universities of Würzburg and Bonn in Germany.

am." I do not suggest that the housewife's despair is a very serious application of the Second Law of Thermodynamics, but people have tried to use the law to understand why living organisms ultimately always "wear out" and thus die, and it has also been suggested that some day our whole universe perhaps must come to a sticky end because everything will finally have got so mixed up and disordered that there will be nothing else left to do with it. Mind you, even the most pessimistic physicist or philosopher has never suggested that this end to the universe would happen by itself in less than thousands of millions of years from now. So this does not give mankind any reason to try to speed up the process by the careless use of hydrogen bombs or the like, which one could certainly say would be one of the *quickest* ways of disordering things and increasing their entropy!

Kelvin's Absolute Scale of Temperature

Well now, we said that high temperatures mean atomic disorder and low temperatures mean order. But how *much* order or disorder? This brings us right away to the second main problem; namely, how do we *measure* how cold or how hot things are? It certainly seems natural to me that there would be some state of perfect *order* in things, but, on the other hand, I can see no obvious reason why you could not go on making things more and more *disorderly* if you tried hard enough.[5] What this would mean is that there must be some *lower* limit of temperature, of "absolute cold," as we might call it, where everything would

[5] Perhaps we might recall the housewife and the children. An (optimistic) housewife might well say: "At last this room is perfectly tidy," and a few hours later might easily say: "There doesn't seem to be *any* limit to how untidy the kids can make this room!"

reach a maximum state of atomic order and would
be "perfectly arranged", but that there would be
no limit in principle to the *highest* temperature
(great atomic disorder) that things might achieve.
This is just about the situation which was clearly
recognized by William Thomson[6] (later Lord Kelvin) about a hundred years ago, when he put forward his *Absolute Scale of Temperature,* which starts
at the bottom at "absolute zero" and goes on up, as
far as we know, without any limit. It then turns
out that the absolute zero of temperature comes at
–273.15°C. On Kelvin's scale we call the absolute
zero 0°K (zero degrees Kelvin), and thus the freezing point of water (the "ice point"), which defines
0°C, comes at +273.15°K, and 100°C (where water
boils normally) comes at +373.15°K. Perhaps Fig. 3
will help you to see how the two scales of temperature
relate to one another.

On this absolute scale of temperature we can now
compare much more readily how cold or how hot
things are in a precise and universal way. For example, air becomes liquid at about 80°K (about

[6] William Thomson (1824–1907) was born in Belfast,
Northern Ireland, into a family of Scottish descent. His fa-
ther, James Thomson, became Professor of Mathematics in
Glasgow University, and William Thomson, after studying
at Glasgow, Cambridge, and Paris, was appointed to the
Chair of Natural Philosophy (Physics) at Glasgow University when he was only twenty-two. He contributed to just
about every known field of physical science, and, when he
was only thirty-four, he was knighted as Sir William Thomson for his pioneer work in the laying of the first Atlantic
cable. William Thomson served for over fifty years as Professor at Glasgow University, and in 1892 Queen Victoria
made him a peer. In thinking of titles such names as Lord
Compass or Lord Cable were suggested, but Thomson finally chose that of Lord Kelvin, after the small river on
whose banks the University of Glasgow stands. He died in
1907 after a most successful and productive career and was
buried near the grave of Sir Isaac Newton, in Westminster
Abbey, in London.

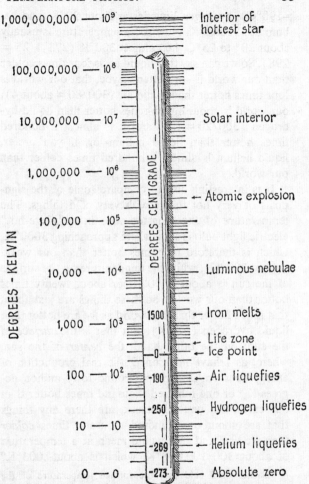

FIG. 3. *This unfamiliar logarithmic scale of temperature is used because certain relationships are easier to picture; for instance, each major division is 10 times the next lower one or 1/10 of the next higher one. A simple chart based upon your household thermometer would have to be 100,000 miles long to show this same information.*

−190°C), hydrogen liquefies at about 20°K, and helium at about 4°K. Now room temperature is usually about 20° to 25°C, i.e., almost 300°K (273 + 25 = 298). So we can say that liquid air is four times colder than our world is—or better maybe, that our world is four times hotter than liquid air (300/80 = about 4); our world is about fifteen times hotter than liquid hydrogen (300/20 = 15), and it is almost a hundred times hotter than liquid helium—or, if you prefer, liquid helium is almost a hundred times colder than our world.

It is interesting also to compare some of the signposts of very hot things with very cold things. The temperature of the tungsten wire in a "white-hot" electric light bulb is somewhere approaching 3000°K, which is therefore ten times hotter than our world (about 300°K), while the temperature on the surface of the sun is about 6000°K, or about twenty times hotter than our world.[7] So these things are just about that much hotter than our world as *we* are hotter than liquid hydrogen (Fig. 4). But that is the *surface* of the sun; on the other hand, the *center* of the sun, where, as I have mentioned, the real production of energy goes on, is perhaps around forty million degrees K,[8] or one hundred thousand times hotter than our earth. So, you might ask, are there any things that are about one hundred thousand times *colder* than we are, and that would mean at a temperature of about 300/100,000°K, which is about .003°K?

[7] Earlier on I said that the surface temperature of the sun was about 6000°C, and you might wonder why I *now* say it is about 6000°K. But you see when we get to these high temperatures it does not matter very much which of the two scales you use, because even if the sun's apparent temperature were precisely 6000°C (which anyway we do not know exactly), its absolute temperature would be 6273°K, which is not really much different from 6000°K.

[8] See also footnote on p. 19.

SUN
surface about 6000°K
or 20 times hotter
than the . . . . .

EARTH
surface about 300°K
or 15 times hotter
than . . . . .

LIQUID HYDROGEN
which boils at 20°K

FIG. 4. *How hot is the sun? How cold is liquid hydrogen?*

Well, as a matter of fact, this is just about the lowest temperature that we can conveniently achieve in a suitably equipped low temperature laboratory today.

Recently I was watching a television program called *Two for Physics* by Doctors J. N. Patrick Hume and Donald G. Ivey of Toronto University, and they suggested that as regards the size of things "man is in the middle." Atoms and nuclei are so much smaller than we are, and star systems and galaxies in the universe are so much larger. We can also say that man is "in the middle" in his knowledge and use of temperature, with things like nuclear explosions at the hot end, and the achievement of very low temperatures for research at the other end. As a matter of fact, although it is very difficult to go much below about .005°K, it has been done in the Clarendon Laboratory in Oxford, England. I shall talk about this sort of thing later when we discuss how we achieve low temperatures, but let us note here that Simon, Kürti, and others in Oxford, using the magnetic properties of nuclei to achieve order, did experiments where they reached temperatures of only a few *millionths* of a degree absolute (a few times .000001°K). Mind you, the vital part of the apparatus did not *stay* very long at this fantastically low temperature (for only about 10 or 20 seconds), but they got there nonetheless. And a temperature as low as this means that they were able to make something about thirty million times colder than our earth! On the other hand, something that much *hotter* than our earth would have a temperature of about 10,000,000,-000°K, and as far as I know no one has ever suggested that temperatures of this magnitude have yet been observed *anywhere!* So in one sense the low temperature physicists are winning the game hands down at the moment; their "cold-making devices" have probed relatively deeper into matter than the "hot-making devices" have been able to do. But remember, all this is really very rough and relative, and of course you must not take this sort of comparison too seriously.

I have mentioned temperatures like .003°K and .000001°K. I think you might well ask whether we can go any lower than this, and if so whether there is any point in it. In other words, is there any need to worry about the last *thousandth,* or the last *millionth,* of a degree above absolute zero? Now in large part the answer to this sort of question leads us to another law of thermodynamics (the Third), which has not proved nearly so interesting to philosophers (and perhaps housewives, as I suggested) as the *Second* law, but it is a most important law in understanding low temperature physics. Roughly speaking, what one can deduce from the Third Law of Thermodynamics is that:

(i) Although the Absolute Zero is a perfectly definite concept (and remember we can fix its temperature at about –273°C), we can never actually achieve *precisely* that state with any physical system.

(ii) Although we can never get to $T = 0°K$ exactly, we can go along the road as far as we choose if we take enough trouble. And how far would we choose to go? Well, to some extent, this question looks after itself. Remember that achieving lower and lower temperatures just means that we are concerned with finer and finer details of the energy of bodies—always assuming there are finer details to be found. So we can say that if there *are* finer details to be found out, it surely will be worth going on to search for them, whether these details lie at 1/10, 1/1000, 1/100,000 or even 1/100,000,000th of a degree above absolute zero. Moreover, if there *are* these details of the energy structure to be found out, then this fact in itself will somehow provide us with a way to get to these lower temperatures. So when, and if, there ever comes a day when there is no more detail to be found in physical systems, then we shall not be able to go any further along the road to absolute zero—and it won't matter anyhow!

Someone once asked Sir Francis Simon,[9] I think: "Do you think the road to absolute zero will ultimately become an uninteresting desert?"; to which Sir Francis replied, more or less: "Well if it becomes a featureless desert, there won't be any way of crossing it, so the question answers itself."

[9] Sir Francis Simon (Franz Eugen Simon, 1893–1956) was originally a pupil of Walther Nernst, a famous German physical chemist. Nernst laid the foundation for the Third Law of Thermodynamics mentioned earlier, and Simon developed this concept clearly and thoroughly through his work in Berlin, and later (after the start of the Hitler regime in Germany) at Oxford University. He died in 1956 after establishing a flourishing laboratory of low temperature research at the Clarendon Laboratory in Oxford. He used to say, rather wryly, that he was probably the only man who had both an Iron Cross of Imperial Germany and a Knighthood of the British Empire!

CHAPTER 2

HOW DO WE MAKE LOW TEMPERATURES?

We have said that low temperatures mean order, and high temperatures disorder on the atomic scale of things. In any particular substance at a given volume the atoms have a more orderly arrangement at a lower temperature than at a higher temperature. So if we want to use something as a refrigerant, we have got to find a way of bringing order into the atomic arrangements. The most natural way to do this is certainly to start with something that is very disordered in the beginning. A gas is a good choice because the atoms are flying about in a very random disordered way. If you took some gas in an insulated cylinder (see Fig. 5) and compressed it by pushing in the piston, then you might think that you would increase the atomic order because you would certainly have forced the atoms more closely together. But this is not so.

When you push in the piston of this insulated cylinder, you not only push the atoms closer together, but you also give them more energy, which comes from the work done by pushing in the piston against the pressure of the gas. Although the atoms of the gas are closer together, at the same time they are also rushing about much more violently than before—put

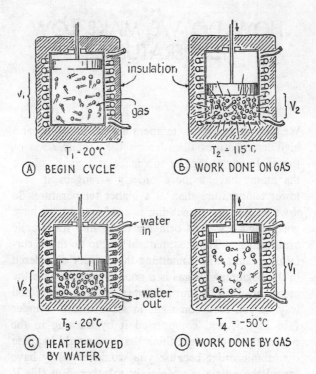

FIG. 5. *How gases may be cooled is shown in this simplified cycle. It assumes perfect insulation and the temperatures are theoretical and idealized.*

PLATE I-A. Experiments at extremely low temperatures (about .01°K). Apparatus being wheeled into powerful magnet.

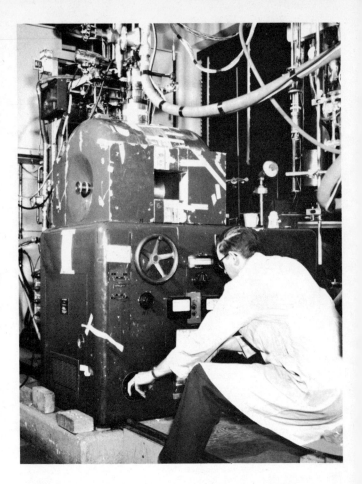

PLATE I-B. Apparatus now in magnet, and magnet current being switched on.

PLATE II. Liquid air being poured out. When it strikes the floor, the liquid air evaporates very rapidly producing a cloud of cold gas because the floor is about four times hotter than the liquid air.

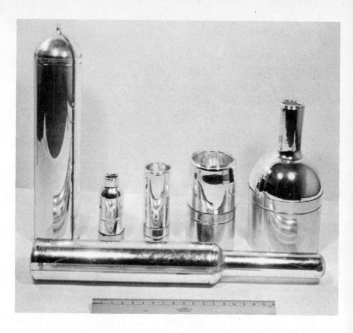

PLATE III. Typical Dewar flasks used in the laboratory.

briefly, you have raised the temperature of the gas by compressing it. It can be shown that, so far, we are no better off than we were when we began; the increased *order* obtained by bringing the atoms close together in space has been cancelled out by the increased *disorder* because they are now flying about much more violently. Indeed, as you can see, far from reducing the temperature, we have *increased* the temperature of the gas! If we started off with air as the gas in the cylinder at room temperature (say 20°C), then by pushing in the piston halfway like this we would raise the gas to a temperature of roughly 115°C. Now let us suppose that instead of keeping the cylinder insulated, but while still keeping the piston pushed in, we make some cold water flow around the outside of the cylinder, cooling the gas down again to room temperature. When that has been done, the gas will certainly be more ordered than it was before, because the atoms are now just moving about at the *same* speed as when we began (because we have brought the temperature back to where we started by using the cold-water jacket); but, on the other hand, the atoms are certainly much closer together than when we began. Altogether we have thus increased the atomic order of the gas atoms or, technically speaking, we have reduced the entropy.

So now, if we are clever enough, we can use this increased order (or reduced entropy) to achieve a low temperature in the gas. We insulate the cylinder once more, and let the piston come back out to where we began the whole business, so letting the gas expand. Because we have kept the cylinder insulated this time, we can argue again that during this second process there will be no over-all change in the total *order* (or disorder!) of the gas atoms. It is certainly true that they are once more taking up more space, so they are more disordered in *that* way, but to make up for this increase of disorder, each atom must have lost some of its "zip"[1] and so be moving about much more sluggishly. In fact, they lost their zip by pushing out the piston for us. What this amounts to is that the gas will now be much cooler than when we started. If we go back to our example of a cylinder with air in it, it would now have cooled ideally to about −50°C. Finally, if we turn this whole business into a regular cycle in some sort of machine, then this process, repeated, offers one of the most important methods of achieving low temperatures.

If we had started off with ammonia gas in this cooling operation, it is quite possible that we could liquefy the gas directly by using a continuous cycle in this way. Ammonia gas becomes liquid at about −30°C, and it would be quite easy to get that temperature drop even in a practical machine allowing for unwanted heat influx and so on. But if we wanted instead to liquefy something like air, which requires going down to a temperature more like −190°C, then it is not difficult to see that one might need to make a machine with successive cycles. For example, we could start by cooling, or liquefying, one gas first, and then use this stage to cool a second gas, and so on further if necessary. And how far could we go with this process? Well, presumably, in theory at least, we could go on until we have made every substance liquid, or for that matter solid. And to understand when this might happen, we have got to think a little more about why one substance becomes a liquid at one temperature, and another at another.

[1] Those who feel outraged by this descriptive slang can substitute the technical expression "kinetic energy."

Atomic Order and Disorder

All atoms are attracted to one another to some extent, but some atoms have stronger attractions than others. Perhaps the simplest case to think about first is a substance like common salt. Common salt is made up of atoms of sodium and chlorine in equal quantities. Now a single sodium atom by itself has no net electric charge on it. It has a nucleus, which has eleven positive charges tucked inside it; there are eleven negatively-charged electrons spinning around outside that nucleus, rather like planets around the sun, and the whole atom together is about a hundred millionth part of an inch across.[2] In sodium the first ten electrons that orbit around the nucleus form a pretty snug and aloof family, leaving the eleventh one, so to speak, as an "outsider" or a "black sheep." Let us remember that. A chlorine atom, on the other hand, has seventeen positive charges in the nucleus, and seventeen (negative) electrons going around outside to keep the whole atom neutral. It turns out that in chlorine we are just one electron short of making up a rather tight "family" of electrons going around the

[2] We owe this "planetary" model of the atom with the positive nucleus as the "sun," and an equal number of negative electrons circling around outside as the planets, making up the neutral atom, to Lord Ernest Rutherford (1871–1937) and Niels (Hendrik David) Bohr (1885–). Rutherford was born in New Zealand and after working at McGill University in Montreal and at Manchester University, he became Cavendish Professor of Physics at Cambridge from 1919. Rutherford's greatest discovery was the concept of the atomic nucleus as the tiny, "hard," central core of the atom. Bohr worked for some time with Rutherford at Manchester. His greatest achievement was to understand how the electrons circling round the nucleus can take up certain stable orbits which determine the physical state of the atom. Both Bohr and Rutherford received Nobel Prizes for their work.

nucleus. So when these two types of atoms (sodium and chlorine) get together, there is a very strong tendency for the "lonely" electron around the sodium atom to be transferred across to the chlorine atom, so completing the family of electrons there. This leaves the sodium atom now with a net *positive* charge of one unit, having lost a negative electron, and gives the chlorine atom an excess *negative* charge of one unit. In those circumstances they are not called atoms any longer, but "ions."[3]

If this pair of sodium and chlorine ions are close enough together, there will now be a strong electric attraction between them because they are charged in this way—one positive and the other negative—and, indeed, this is the main force that binds together sodium and chlorine atoms in equal numbers to form a piece of common salt, whose chemical name is sodium chloride. The electric forces holding together these charged sodium and chlorine atoms (chemists call it the "ionic bond") are so strong that it needs a temperature of at least 800°C to give the atoms enough energy to fly apart from one another with the salt vaporizing to form a gas.

Now in *other* substances the forces of attraction are not always as strong. In water, which is all around us, each molecule is made up of two atoms of hydrogen and one of oxygen, and in each of these water molecules the hydrogen and oxygen atoms are quite strongly tied together, in something like the same way

---

[3] The word *ion* comes originally from a Greek word meaning "to go." If you dissolve common salt in water, the atoms break up into the positively charged sodium atoms, and negatively charged chlorine atoms. These charged atoms can then "wander" through the water, and carry an electric current (precisely because they *are* charged), and hence comes the name "ion" or "wanderer" for an atom with a net electric charge.

that the sodium and chlorine atoms of salt are bound together. When you bring water molecules close together, however, the molecules do have *some* attraction for each other, but this is not nearly so strong as the atomic attraction. We need heat up water only to about 100°C, as you know, for each water molecule to get enough energy to fly away from its neighbors, in that case forming steam or water vapor.

If we turn finally to the lightest and simplest elements, such as a helium atom or a hydrogen molecule, then we find that the forces between the atoms or molecules are extremely weak. This means that even at very low temperatures the atoms or molecules of these light elements are still quite free to fly about in all directions as a gas. Thus, even when these light gases are very cold, there is still plenty of disorder left among the atoms, and we can therefore make use of these gases to achieve extremely low temperatures. It turns out that the weakest interaction forces of all are found between helium atoms, and the force is so weak that at temperatures above about 4° Kelvin (about −269°C), the atoms will not "stick" together and helium remains a gas.[4] However, at about 4°K helium does finally liquefy,[5] while at this very low temperature all *other* substances have long since turned into solids. The temperature is so low that the thermal movement of the helium atoms has become

[4] We discuss this question of interatomic forces a bit more in Chapter 4 when we consider more specifically the behavior of liquid helium itself.

[5] The temperature at which a gas turns into a liquid depends also on the pressure of the gas. Generally speaking, when we refer to a gas's liquefying or a liquid's "boiling" we mean at one atmosphere pressure (about 15 pounds per square inch, or about one kg per square centimeter) unless someone says otherwise. Helium boils at one atmosphere pressure at 4.2°K, but if we raise the pressure to two atmospheres, it will boil at 5.04°K.

very faint, and even the weak force between these atoms is just strong enough to bind them all together.

But although the force between the helium atoms is just strong enough to hold them together as a *liquid* below about 4°K, it is not strong enough to hold the very light helium atoms together to form a *solid*. As a matter of fact, at around 4°K we have to give them a help by applying quite a strong pressure from the outside (about 100 atmospheres or around 1500 pounds to the square inch) to enable the helium atoms to form a solid in which the atoms are arranged in a regular pattern. Helium is the only substance where this happens. In all other substances, if you make them sufficiently cold, the forces between the atoms are strong enough by themselves to array the atoms in a more or less regular pattern; the atoms fit into one another something like the cells in a beehive. But helium is a striking exception; the interatomic forces just can pull the atoms together to make a liquid, but are not strong enough by themselves to form a solid. We shall have something more to say about this in Chapter 4.

Now, once we have got liquid helium boiling at about 4°K, can we get to any lower temperatures, or is this the limit? If we connect a vacuum pump to the liquid helium in order to draw off the vapor very rapidly, then we shall find that the liquid will become colder. This behavior is quite general for *all* liquids, and it is not difficult to see why. The atoms that pop out of a liquid to form the vapor surrounding it are those that have a bit more energy or "zip" than the average. If you keep taking away these more energetic atoms all the time by means of a vacuum pump, the atoms that are left in the liquid tend, naturally enough, to be more and more the sluggish members of the party—that is, the ones with the least energy stay behind, and therefore the remaining liquid must get colder. With a very large and powerful vacuum pump it is possible to reduce the temperature of liquid helium down to as low as about 0.8°K. We must accept this 0.8°K as just about the ultimate limit by this method, because now the remaining liquid is so cold that, broadly speaking, none of the atoms has enough energy to "climb out" from the liquid and form a vapor at all; in other words, there is not really any vapor left for us to pump off. While the vapor at 4.2°K exerted a pressure of one atmosphere, down at 1°K it can exert a pressure of only about a ten thousandth part of an atmosphere (more exactly, a pressure of about 0.12 mm of mercury).

"Magnetic Cooling"

Until recently this temperature was indeed the limit we could reach without turning to an entirely different method, which involves the *magnetic* properties of matter. But within the last few years we have been able to use a somewhat different "kind" of helium for getting to lower temperatures. The usual kind of helium atom to be found in the gas from oil wells, or in rather small quantities in the atmosphere, weighs about four times more than a hydrogen atom, and it is known as "helium four" (symbol He⁴). But there is a much rarer type of helium atom with only three-quarters of this weight, which is known as "helium three" (He³).[6] These two types of helium atoms are called "isotopes"; isotopes of any chemical element are atoms that behave more or less the same chemically but have different masses. Now, because each

[6] We shall also discuss the behavior of liquid He³ again in Chapter 4 when we consider the properties of liquid helium in more detail.

He³ atom is considerably lighter than an He⁴ atom, the interatomic forces have an even harder job to hold the atoms together, and in fact you have to go down to about 3°K before *this* kind of "light" helium will liquefy (i.e., under one atmosphere pressure). Correspondingly then, if we make liquid helium from this "light" helium (which is still rather rare today and only to be found in a few laboratories), the vapor will still be usable down to a much lower temperature than that of liquid He⁴. By pumping liquid He³ with a vacuum pump, we can get to even lower temperatures—in fact, down to about 0.4°K—without too much difficulty.

But as far as we know today, 0.4°K really is the limit we can achieve using this sort of system. It seems that nature cannot make lighter helium atoms than He³; hence, as I have suggested, we have to look for some quite different method if we are to try to go still lower in temperature. This question was studied by Debye and Giauque[7] as long ago as 1926, and the problem is simply to see if we can discover any properties of matter that remain disordered on an atomic scale even at these extremely low temperatures. That is, we want to find some source of entropy

[7] Peter (Joseph Wilhelm) Debye (1884–   ) was born in the Netherlands. After working at various universities in Europe, he came to the United States in 1940. He has contributed very widely to physical chemistry, and particularly to our understanding of solids. His theory of the thermal vibrations of a solid (1911) is among his best-known work. He received the Nobel Prize in Chemistry in 1936. William Francis Giauque (1895–   ) was born in Canada, at Niagara Falls, Ontario. He has been professor at the University of California, Berkeley, for over twenty years. Almost simultaneously, and independently, Giauque and Debye proposed that paramagnetic salts could be used for achieving very low temperatures. Giauque also received a Nobel Prize for his work.

(atomic disorder) which we can make use of to push down even further in temperature.[8]

Debye and Giauque turned to the magnetic properties of matter, and in particular to what are known as the paramagnetic salts (such substances as iron ammonium alum, chromium potassium alum, and cerium magnesium nitrate). Let us have a look at the first of these salts. In iron ammonium alum each iron atom behaves as a tiny magnet, and each of these atomic magnets is well separated from the other little iron atom magnets by all the other kinds of atoms making up the substance.[9] Because the iron atoms are well separated, the magnetic forces between them are very weak. This means that each little magnet "belonging" to an iron atom is almost perfectly free to point in any direction, and this freedom in itself immediately implies a high degree of atomic disorder or entropy. Now when we discussed the use of gases to get to low temperatures, I mentioned that we could use a piston to alter the volume of the gas and ultimately change the entropy. The piston, you will remember, can exert forces on the gas molecules and so alter their energy. Now what must we use if we are trying to alter the energy of the atomic magnets? The answer is a magnetic field. And what we have to do to achieve very low temperatures is to carry through a cycle of operations on the magnetic properties of matter. Instead of pushing a piston in and

[8] Sir Francis Simon often used to use phrases like "sucking out the entropy" when referring to achieving low temperatures. This is very apt; and not only do you have to suck out the entropy, but you have to find some entropy to suck!

[9] The chemical formula of iron ammonium alum is $FeNH_4(SO_4)_2, 12H_2O$; you can see that there are indeed lots of other atoms there as well as the all-important iron ones.

out of a cylinder to compress and rarify a gas, we apply a very powerful magnet to act on the magnetic atoms. I have tried in Fig. 6 to illustrate this cycle of operations, which enables us to reach temperatures well below 1°K. Plate I also shows a quite typical apparatus being used in this way.

We saw that the limit of using a gas for reaching low temperatures was essentially set by the temperature at which the gas will liquefy; i.e., the temperature where the random thermal energy of the atoms becomes weak enough to allow the forces between the atoms to hold them together. For the paramagnetic salts a corresponding situation arises at a very low temperature when even the tiny magnetic forces between individual iron atoms, for example, prove sufficient to line them up with one another. At that temperature one might say that the substance had "solidified magnetically,"[10] becoming magnetically ordered, whereas at higher temperatures it was behaving like a "magnetic gas," with each atomic magnet pointing at random, independent of its neighbors. The whole point of using these paramagnetic salts with magnetic atoms separated far from one another is that the magnetic forces acting *between* these atoms are so small that the temperature where the atomic magnets tend to line up spontaneously with one another is very low indeed (e.g., for iron ammonium alum about .04°K, and for cerium magnesium nitrate

[10] Technically this temperature would be known as the Curie temperature, or Néel temperature, where a substance becomes either ferromagnetic or what is called anti-ferromagnetic. In a ferromagnetic substance the individual atomic magnets line up *parallel* with one another as in a piece of iron at normal temperatures, a condition which can make the substance a powerful magnet. In an anti-ferromagnetic body the atomic magnets tend to line up alternately in *opposite* directions.

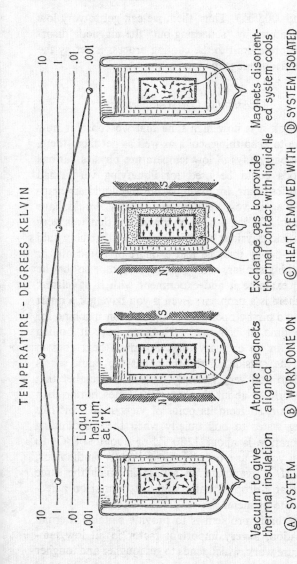

TEMPERATURE – DEGREES KELVIN

10
1
.01
.001

Liquid
helium
at 1°K

Vacuum to give
thermal insulation

Atomic magnets
aligned

Exchange gas to provide
thermal contact with liquid He

Magnets disorient-
ed system cools

(A) SYSTEM
ISOLATED

(B) WORK DONE ON
SYSTEM BY MAGNET

(C) HEAT REMOVED WITH
EXCHANGE GAS

(D) SYSTEM ISOLATED
MAGNET REMOVED

FIG. 6. *Gases may be cooled further by the use of paramagnetic salts. This is the idealized cycle.*

around .005°K). Thus, then, we can get to very low temperatures by "squeezing out" the magnetic disorder before a limit to the cooling process is set by the spontaneous magnetic interaction.

Sustaining Low Temperatures

I think it is now high time that we consider how we are to *keep* things cold, as well as get them there. In the early days of low temperature physics various methods could be used for liquefying very small quantities of air, for example, but the liquid air evaporated again very rapidly, and all one would have was a quick "snapshot" of something that was very cold. One physicist remarked in effect that he would not be happy until he had a quart of liquid air, or something similar, boiling quietly in a tube so that he could examine it and experiment with it at leisure. But there is a problem: Even if you have got a quart of liquid air by operating a liquefaction machine for some time, it is rather difficult to have it boiling quietly in an ordinary tube. So much heat goes in from the outside all the time that the liquid air is liable to boil very violently indeed! Remember that our world is about three or four times hotter than liquid air, so from its point of view it is a bit like asking water to boil quietly when the surrounding temperature is about 1200°K, or about 900°C! In fact, if you pour a little liquid air directly on the floor, Plate II, it evaporates in a flash in much the same way that a drop of water would if poured on a red-hot plate of metal.

The basic problem is to provide suitable thermal insulation, a very important factor in all low temperature work, which tends to get tougher and tougher as we go to lower and lower temperatures. The most important single invention was certainly the Dewar[11] flask (otherwise known as a "Thermos" vacuum bottle). In this device we have two glass flasks, one inside the other and a good vacuum between, so that there is no air left to carry heat from the outer flask to the inner one. In addition, the walls of the glass vessels that face one another are silvered (see Fig. 7 and Plate III), as silvering prevents radiation from taking heat directly from the outside to the inside of the vessel. With these vessels it is not only possible to keep soup and tea very hot, as I am sure you know, but also to keep liquids inside very cold. The two principles of the Dewar flask—that of providing a high vacuum to insulate a container thermally from its surroundings, and the use of shiny metal surfaces to reflect away unwanted radiation—are basic today in the design of any apparatus which is to operate at very low temperatures.

Well now, if we have first made liquid air, then produced some liquid helium, and finally gone on from there to use a paramagnetic salt together with a powerful magnet to get down to perhaps 0.01°K, have we ultimately reached the limit of low temperatures? Not really; recently Kürti and Simon in Oxford went yet another stage further. Instead of using the magnetic properties of an atom as a *whole,* they now managed to make use of just the magnetic properties of the *nuclei* of atoms to provide an entropy source to enable them to reach extremely low temperatures. They had to *start* their work at about 0.01°K (having used the various other methods we have already

[11] Sir James Dewar (1842–1923) was Professor of Chemistry at the Royal Institution of London and later became Director of the Davy-Faraday Research Laboratory. Dewar in 1898 first liquefied hydrogen, which boils under one atmosphere pressure at about 20.4°K, and the next year he reached the freezing point of hydrogen (about 14°K).

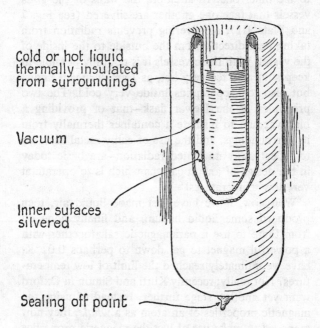

Cold or hot liquid
thermally insulated
from surroundings

Vacuum

Inner sufaces
silvered

Sealing off point

FIG. 7.   *A diagram of the familiar Dewar flask similar to the one carried in a lunch box.*

discussed to get there in the first place), and then they applied a very strong magnetic field (about a hundred thousand times that of the earth) in order to "squeeze out" some entropy from the nuclear magnetic system. With these experiments Dr. Kürti has managed to go down to temperatures somewhere around $10^{-5\circ}$ to $10^{-6\circ}$K (i.e., approaching one millionth of a degree above the absolute zero!).

Apart from the enormous difficulty of reaching such a fantastically low temperature (and let me remind you that by comparison our world is about a hundred million times hotter), one runs into increasing problems of keeping anything that cold for very long. The trouble is this. If a given quantity of heat manages to get into some container at a low temperature, then the "damage" it does, in the sense of creating atomic disorder and so raising the temperature, is greater in inverse proportion to the temperature. Very roughly speaking, if we had an apparatus at $1\circ$K and managed to keep the unwanted heat flow down to a value that would cause the apparatus to warm up a few degrees in perhaps twenty-four hours, this same heat flow would cause a similar apparatus at $.01\circ$K to warm up to perhaps $1\circ$K in about a quarter of an hour (fifteen minutes). And if our apparatus started at $.00001\circ$K, it might well warm up with the same heat flow in about a second! So not only does it get harder and harder to reach lower and lower temperatures, but it gets tougher and tougher to keep things there once you have reached a low temperature. I mentioned at the beginning of this book that low temperature physics was rather like mountaineering in some ways, and once again it seems to me the situation is quite similar. I think I am right in saying that when Mount Everest was finally climbed it became harder and harder to climb the last few stages to the very top; in fact, the climbers stayed on the summit for only a very few minutes before having to start down again.

If we ask once more whether we really have reached the limit of low temperatures *this* time by using the magnetic properties of the atomic nucleus, I must remind you of what we said at the end of Chapter 1. If anything remarkable goes on happening at these extremely low temperatures, then we can probably make use of that behavior to get down to even lower temperatures, to find out if anything is happening *there*. And if anything is happening at these lower temperatures, then maybe we can use those properties to go on down to still lower temperatures. . . . Certainly the story has not finished yet, and I for one would not be rash enough to predict that it must stop somewhere!

CHAPTER 3

CONDUCTIVITY AND SUPERCONDUCTIVITY

One of the most remarkable things found at very low temperatures is the phenomenon of superconductivity. But before we consider superconductivity itself, let me recall one or two things about common- or garden-variety electrical conductivity—that is to say, the behavior of most metals. We saw earlier that if we have a piece of metal and apply an electric voltage to it, then this voltage tends to drive the electrons, which constitute the electric current, through that metal. If *nothing* stopped these electrons, they would go faster and faster, and the electric current would continue to grow without limit so long as we applied the voltage to the metal. If at any time we should remove the voltage, we would expect the current to continue flowing at the same rate since there would be nothing to stop the electrons. However, we would expect the electrons to flow through undisturbed only if the atoms in the metal were arranged in an *absolutely* perfect pattern, with no imperfection of any kind whatsoever to spoil the atomic arrangement.

But real metals are never perfect, and, generally speaking, the imperfections are of two kinds. There will always be some "foreign" or "impurity" atoms present, which we call chemical imperfections, and there will also always be some *physical* defects in the metal structure—the metal has been physically strained in some way or another and the atoms no longer form a regular and perfect pattern. Consequently, the flowing electrons making up the electric current will be scattered from time to time by these imperfections in a metal; the moving electrons constantly will be thrown out of their regular paths by these defects of one kind or another.

This scattering requires us to apply a steady force to the electrons (which is just what the electric voltage provides) to keep them moving through the metal and so maintain a steady electric current. In addition to these chemical and physical defects causing electrical resistance in the metal, heat enters the picture. Heat, we must also remember, causes the atoms in a metal to vibrate thermally, and this vibration gets stronger as we increase the temperature. These heat vibrations of the atoms make it more difficult for the electrons to fight their way through and as a result also lead to electrical resistivity. Now, as we cool a piece of metal down, the thermal vibrations of the atoms get less and less, and once we have reached a very low temperature, such as that of liquid helium, the thermal vibrations of the atoms become very small; the only electrical resistance left then, in general, is that due to the impurity atoms or physical strains of one kind or another in the metal.

Resistance at Low Temperatures

So, one should expect that if you cool down any particular metal, its electrical resistance should go down to a low value, and the purer the metal the lower should be that value. If we start off with a piece of fairly pure copper wire which has been suitably heat-treated (annealed) to eliminate most of the physical strain, and which has an electrical resistance of perhaps 300 ohms at room temperature, then by the time we have cooled it down to the temperature of liquid helium its resistance may well be only 1 ohm. But once we have reached this limiting resistance at low temperatures due to these defects, we should not expect any further change if we reduce the temperature still further (see Fig. 8A). Behavior of this sort is what in fact we find for many metals. The electrical resistance that is left at the lowest temperatures is often called the *residual resistance* and can be a very useful thing to study.

On the one hand, this residual resistance gives a useful, although somewhat rough-and-ready, measurement of the over-all degree of perfection of the metal. If the metal is very pure and free from strain (Fig. 8B), then naturally the residual resistance is very low (perhaps as small as *.0001* of the room-temperature resistance), while in a much less pure piece of metal the resistance might fall to perhaps only a quarter of its room-temperature value when it is placed in liquid helium. Quite recently in our work we obtained from a company specializing in this sort of thing a set of alloys which they had prepared for us. Since some other measurements we were making suggested that something was peculiar about one or two of these alloys, we made measurements of the residual resistance in liquid helium. In one particular alloy the residual resistance was about ten times higher than we expected, and led us to believe that some additional impurity or defect must be present in that metal. The supplier checked the purity with spectrographic analysis, and, sure enough, found that some unintended contamination had crept into that particular alloy.

Apart from that sort of *practical* application,

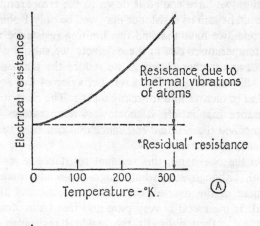

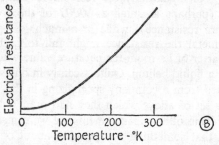

FIG. 8. *Sketched graph of how the electrical resist-ance of metals varies with temperature. (A) A metal with a fair amount of chemical impurity or physical imperfection present. (B) A rather pure, well an-nealed piece of metal.*

measurements of electrical resistance are of great value in comparing the amount of scattering that electrons suffer from various causes in a metal, with what *theory* has to tell us. Today it is very important to try to understand more about the causes of strength (or perhaps weakness) in certain metals. It is now known that the regular atomic pattern in a metal can be disturbed in places by what is known as a *dislocation*. It is a little like the situation where you have a lot of small bubbles forming a regular pattern on the surface of tea in a cup, and the pattern breaks up because some of the bubbles burst or because some bubbles are larger than others. (See Plates IV and V.) These dislocations in the atomic pattern play an important part in influencing the strength of a metal, and it becomes important to know as much as we can about them and their behavior. At the same time, since they do disturb the regular pattern of the atoms, the dislocations also will scatter the conduction electrons and so produce electrical resistance. Hence, by measuring the electrical resistance, we may be able to compare in various situations whether the atomic dislocations are affecting the electrons in the way we thought they did, and so in turn we can check whether our theoretical ideas are sound or not. On the other hand, if we have a very carefully annealed piece of metal, to eliminate the physical strains, and measure the resistance at low temperatures, we may be pretty certain that almost all the remaining electrical resistance is due to some kind of foreign atom. Then we can predict the amount of scattering of electrons from our theoretical ideas of how an impurity atom behaves in a metal, and compare the prediction with what we observe experimentally in the laboratory from our measurement of resistance.

Discovery of Superconductivity

These are some examples of how studying the electrical resistance of metals can help us to solve other problems about the behavior of metals. Shortly after he had first liquefied helium in 1908, Kamerlingh Onnes[1] and his colleagues at Leiden, in the Netherlands, started to do a series of experiments on the electrical resistance of metals at very low temperatures. One of the first metals studied was mercury. I think one good reason for this choice was that it is rather easy to purify mercury quite highly without a great deal of expensive equipment. When the electrical resistance of mercury near the temperature of liquid helium was measured, the Leiden workers found that the resistance had dropped a long way from the value it had at room temperature, perhaps to a hundredth part of its original value. But when the temperature had actually reached that of boiling liquid helium (about 4.2° Kelvin), the electrical resistance appeared to *vanish* quite suddenly. Now at this point I want to make something quite clear. We know today with almost absolute certainty that the resistance of a metal such as mercury down at these

[1] Heike Kamerlingh Onnes (1853–1926) was Professor of Physics at the University of Leiden from 1882, and in 1913 received the Nobel Prize in Physics for his accomplishment in liquefying helium and for his subsequent research at these very low temperatures. Hendrik Antoon Lorentz (1853–1928), also born in 1853, died two years after Onnes. He was a most brilliant Dutch theoretical physicist of world-renown who shared with Pieter Zeeman (yet another distinguished Dutch physicist) the Nobel Prize in Physics in 1902. To commemorate the work of these two great Dutch scientists a Kamerlingh Onnes-Lorentz Centenary Congress was held in Leiden in 1953 at the Kamerlingh Onnes Laboratory.

low temperatures does vanish absolutely and completely. It is not merely that the resistance drops to a low value (although in fact Kamerlingh Onnes was not quite certain of that when he first discovered the effect), but we believe now, and I shall mention the experimental proof later, that the resistance vanishes completely—and that is why this particularly striking behavior in certain metals at low temperatures is known as superconductivity.[2]

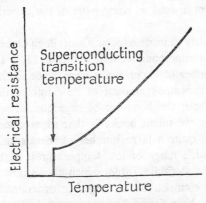

FIG. 9. *Sketched curve to show how the electrical resistance of a pure unstrained superconductor vanishes abruptly at low temperatures.*

There are two most remarkable features about superconductivity. First, the resistance does not simply "fade away" but, as we cool a pure, unstrained piece of metal, we find that at some particular temperature the resistance drops to zero with very little "warning," if any at all, of what is going to happen (Fig. 9.). Sec-

2 Sometimes (but less often) it is called supraconductivity. Perhaps this is really a better name meaning "above and beyond" ordinary conductivity.

ondly, the resistance seems to vanish *absolutely* and *completely* when a metal becomes superconducting. Now this sort of occurrence is really rather astonishing. If there were any impurity atoms present, or physical strains—and there must always be some in any real piece of metal—you would expect that those defects would scatter the electrons to some extent and so produce *some* electrical resistance. This behavior therefore posed a very serious problem to the theoretical physicists. But before we talk about theory, let us look at some more of the experimental effects.

For thirty years or so after Kamerlingh Onnes's discovery of superconductivity, about 1911, a tremendous number of experiments were made in this field and an enormous amount of new information obtained about the behavior of superconductors. The first thing we might notice is that superconductivity occurs in quite a large number of metals, and over quite a wide range of low temperatures. In Fig. 10 we see the Periodic Table, which shows how all the chemical elements are arranged in order, and those that have been found to be superconducting at low

---

FIG. 10.   *The periodic table of chemical elements. The number above the element, which determines its position in the periodic table, is called the Atomic Number; it is the number of electrons which orbit around the nucleus in that element. Those elements which become superconducting are shaded, and the temperature at which they first become superconducting as we cool them down is shown underneath each element. (These superconducting temperatures are from the book* Superconductivity *by D. Shoenberg, Cambridge University Press, 1952.)*

PERIODIC TABLE OF CHEMICAL ELEMENTS

SUPERCONDUCTORS SHOWN IN ITALICS WITH TEMPERATURE OF SUPERCONDUCTING TRANSITION

IA	IIA	IIIB	IVB	VB	VIB	VIIB	VIIIB			IB	IIB	IIIA	IVA	VA	VIA	VIIA	VIIIA
H 1																	He 2
Li 3	Be 4											B 5	C 6	N 7	O 8	F 9	Ne 10
Na 11	Mg 12											*Al 13 1.20°K*	Si 14	P 15	S 16	Cl 17	A 18
K 19	Ca 20	Sc 21	*Ti 22 0.53°K*	*V 23 5.1°K*	Cr 24	Mn 25	Fe 26	Co 27	Ni 28	Cu 29	*Zn 30 0.91°K*	*Ga 31 1.10°K*	Ge 32	As 33	Se 34	Br 35	Kr 36
Rb 37	Sr 38	Y 39	*Zr 40 0.70°K*	*Nb(Cb) 41 8°K*	Mo 42	Tc 43	*Ru 44 0.47°K*	Rh 45	Pd 46	Ag 47	*Cd 48 0.56°K*	*In 49 3.37°K*	*Sn 50 3.730°K*	Sb 51	Te 52	I 53	Xe 54
Cs 55	Ba 56	*La 57 4.37°K*	*Hf 72 0.35°K*	*Ta 73 4.4°K*	W 74	*Re 75 1.0°K*	*Os 76 0.71°K*	Ir 77	Pt 78	Au 79	*Hg 80 4.152°K*	*Tl 81 2.38°K*	*Pb 82 7.22°K*	Bi 83	Po 84	At 85	Rn(Em) 86
Fr 87	Ra 88	Ac 89	*														
*			*Ce 58*	Pr 59	Nd 60	Pm 61	Sm 62	Eu 63	Gd 64	Tb 65	Dy 66	Ho 67	Er 68	Tm 69	Yb 70	Lu 71	
			Th 90 1.39°K	Pa 91	*U 92 0.8°K*												

temperatures are indicated by shaded boxes. One sees that while there is quite a variety of different metals that become superconductors, yet in some groups of well-known metals none shows this behavior. In particular, the monovalent group IA metals, the so-called *alkali metals,* which include lithium, sodium, potassium, rubidium and caesium, are *not* superconductors, at least so far as we know today. Also the group IB monovalent metals, gold, silver and copper, show no trace of superconductivity. For those elements that do become superconducting, we find that there is quite a wide range of temperatures at which superconductivity first makes its appearance in any particular element. At present it appears that the element which shows superconductivity at the highest temperature is columbium (known also as niobium), which becomes superconducting at about 8° above the absolute zero. The one that becomes superconducting at the lowest temperature is ruthenium, which loses all its resistance at about 0.5°K.

Now I think you might well ask immediately how one knows that some of the other metals, such as the alkali metals, will not become superconducting if you go *sufficiently* low in temperature. Let us assume that so far careful measurements have been made on the resistance of sodium down to about 0.1°K without finding any signs of superconductivity. If now we make a fresh series of measurements down to 0.01°K, might it not turn out that sodium would be superconductive *there?* Well, this is not an easy question to answer; one must be honest and say right away that there is no guarantee of an absolute nature that this might not happen. On the other hand, we can use some general predictions of theory to guide us, as we shall see shortly; in addition, the very fact that not one metal from group IA or IB has yet shown superconductivity at any temperature where experiments of this kind have been made at least suggests that there is some particular character about these metal groups, that superconductivity just will not occur at all.

Experiments were not only made on various metal elements, but were also extended to include alloys and other intermetallic compounds. Among the superconducting alloys or compounds one finds substances where both constituent metals are themselves superconductors, or where only one member is a superconductor, or even where neither member is itself a superconductor, and yet the compound becomes superconducting. An example is the compound Au_2Bi; neither gold (Au) nor bismuth (Bi) by itself is a superconductor, and yet this compound becomes superconducting if we reduce the temperature to 1.7°K.

Superconductivity and Magnetism

It might well occur to any boy who has tried to produce magnetic fields with a solenoid that superconductors might be very useful for this sort of purpose. After all, one of the difficult things about generating magnetic fields in this way is that the solenoid uses electrical power and heats up when you pass a strong electric current through it. But if a superconducting metal has no resistance at all, presumably one ought to be able to produce a magnetic field without generating heat or wasting any energy. This idea does in fact seem to have occurred to physicists quite early in the history of superconductivity, and the fact that you cannot achieve as much as you would like in this way reveals one of the most important properties of a superconductor. It was discovered that when a superconductor is carrying an electric current, and if the current is raised to a certain critical magnitude,[3] then the superconductor stops being a perfect conductor and reverts to the ordinary resistance one would expect at this temperature. So this phenomenon sets a very definite limit to the size of the current we can pass through a superconducting coil without resistance, and this limitation of current in turn sets severe limits to the magnetic field we can get.

Since we were trying to produce a magnetic field, one might wonder whether the magnetic field itself has something to do with causing this change from superconductivity to ordinary resistance, and indeed it does. If, instead of passing a sufficiently strong current through the superconductor, one simply brings a strong enough magnet near the metal, then the superconductivity vanishes and the conductor goes back to its ordinary resistance. We find that the magnetic field necessary at any given temperature to "destroy" superconductivity is bigger the lower the temperature, and this dependence of critical magnetic field on temperature is a very important feature both in helping theorists to understand the nature of superconductivity, and in practical applications.

Superconductors already are used in quite a number of practical applications which depend often on their role as very efficient, rapid, miniature "switches." Two German scientists, Meissner and Ochsenfeld, showed in 1933 that the magnetic field behavior could be used as an ideal switching device.

---

[3] The actual value of the current depends on the particular superconducting material, on the temperature (which must of course be below the critical temperature at which superconductivity occurs in that particular material), and on the size and shape of the superconductor.

That is to say, you could turn a particular superconducting metal, at least if it was reasonably pure and unstrained and so on, very quickly and completely back and forward from superconducting to normal resistance just by switching on and off the magnetic field. This basic property of a good superconductor has been applied in two sorts of ways through the fertile brains of applied physicists and engineers.

A very interesting idea occurs if you think of taking a piece of superconducting wire and bending it around to form a circle, so joining it up on itself. If somehow you start a current flowing in the wire, this current, just because the material has no electrical resistance, will go on and on around without needing anything further to keep it going. This effect is known as the *persistent current* of a superconductor. And in a sense you might say therefore that the superconducting ring has an extremely good and efficient electrical "memory." You "tell" the superconducting ring to pass a current of one ampere, for example, just now, and if you *keep* the ring superconducting, then you can find out long afterward what current it was that you set going, because it will never have changed. This memory feature offers one of the most important practical applications of superconductors. Thus, in large automatic computers the effect can be used to provide the machine with a "memory"—at least for figures! This behavior also provides much the most sensitive test of whether the resistance really does vanish. Even an extremely tiny resistance in the metal would cause the current to vanish within an hour or so at most. I believe that in one laboratory in the United States, a persistent current of this kind in a superconductor has kept going without ceasing, or at least without changing by any measurable amount, for something over two years—by now it may well be for much longer. So it seems pretty safe to say that the resistance of a superconducting metal is really zero.

Planck's Constant

Now what can we make of superconductivity? The problem was a great challenge to theoreticians for many years, but it does seem as if a fair understanding has come in sight in the last few years. In order to appreciate this, we have to go back now to some very fundamental ideas in physics. We might imagine that if you could really cool down a metal, or any other solid, right to absolute zero, then the atoms of which it is made would become absolutely still, and form a perfectly regular pattern of stationary atoms. Now this sort of picture, the picture of so-called "classical" physics, was assumed to be quite correct until some fifty or sixty years ago. This idea that we could in principle reduce atoms to a state of complete rest so that their velocity was zero and their position precisely fixed corresponded to the belief that there was *in principle* no ultimate limit to the precision with which something could be measured—at least, if you tried hard enough. In other words, if you were prepared to exercise enough patience, you could find out as much detail about anything as you liked. Of course, this does not mean that in practice it would be simple. Scientists knew very well that one would have to develop finer and finer instruments with increasing care. But, I repeat, the belief was there that no final limit existed on the ultimate precision of measurement.

Today, however, we know that there is indeed a very definite and ultimate limit to the accuracy with which things can be observed. This limit is a very remote one which does not normally intrude on our daily life in any way, but it does restrict the accuracy with which you can observe, or even define, atomic behavior. This limit is bound up with a fundamental constant of nature,[4] named after Max Planck,[5] the great German physicist who died just after World War II, and who laid the foundations with Einstein around 1900 of what is now called the *quantum theory*. The quantum theory[6] was born when Planck and Einstein came to realize that the exchange of energy from one form to another was not a completely smooth process. It appeared that energy came only in little "chunks" or bits, or in what are now called *quanta*. If an atom was supposed to be vibrating with a frequency, ν, then the energy associated with that vibration could only exist in little bits of amount $E = h\nu$, where h is Planck's constant. Now if the atom is vibrating at even ten million times a second ($\nu = 10^7$/sec), then since h equals about 6×10^{-27} erg sec, these little bits of energy are only about 10^{-20} ergs—that is, about a hundred million million millionth part of an erg. If you remember that an erg is about the energy that a flea would gain from gravity in dropping about 1 centimeter (less than half

[4] Planck's constant, denoted by h, has the value 6.6×10^{-27} erg sec. Very frequently it occurs in the combination $h/2\pi$, in which case it is denoted by $\hbar$, so that $\hbar = 1.05 \times 10^{-27}$ erg sec.

[5] Max Planck (1858–1947) became Professor at the University of Berlin in 1889, holding his appointment for about forty years, and in 1930 he became President of the Kaiser Wilhelm Institute in Berlin. He received the Nobel Prize in Physics in 1918. Although his formula for electromagnetic radiation was really the start of *quantum physics,* Planck himself was somewhat reluctant to believe that the change of outlook involved was as fundamental as it now appears to be.

[6] The word *quantum* is of Latin origin and simply means a bit or a piece.

an inch), you can see that 10^{-20} ergs is a pretty tiny bit of energy which would not normally worry us! However, Werner Heisenberg[7] pointed out in 1927 that there is a very important consequence of this quantization or "chunkiness" of energy. It means that even if we do all we can to remove all sources of atomic vibration from a substance, in particular by cooling it down as far as possible, Planck's constant effectively sets a limit to our efforts in this direction. So long as we think of a solid as a collection of atoms, then there is a minimum energy that these atoms will appear to have, and this minimum is fixed by Planck's constant.

Now, from our present point of view this means that even at the very lowest temperatures the atoms in a metal or any other solid body still seem to have some vibrations. This energy is known as the *zero-point* vibration of the atoms. Moreover, there are so many atoms in a solid, and they can vibrate in so many ways, that the total amount of this zero-point energy is by no means negligible although each quantum or bit of energy is extremely small. We want to find out what effect this zero-point energy of the atoms can have on the electrons in a metal which provide the electric current.

The zero-point vibrations of the atoms cannot themselves cause any electrical resistance in a metal, because the electrons would have to be able to get some energy from the zero-point vibrations of the atoms. But this is impossible. As I said, the zero-point vibrations are the *minimum* energy that atoms can have, and, naturally, they have none to spare to scatter the electrons. But although they cannot scat-

[7] W. Heisenberg (1901–   ), distinguished German physicist who contributed vitally to the development of quantum mechanics and received the Nobel Prize in Physics in 1932.

ter the electrons to produce electrical resistance, the zero-point vibrations can have an influence on the over-all behavior of the electrons. One possible picture seems to be, put very crudely, that the zero-point vibrations of the atoms, the ones you can never get rid of, can "sweep" the electrons along with them to some extent. If the zero-point vibrations of the atoms are strong enough—you might say if they are sufficiently persuasive—then they are so effective in sweeping the electrons along with them that the electrons ignore any *other* disturbances which they might meet, so long as these imperfections are not too great. In that case, if the temperature is low enough, we get superconductivity, that is to say, a current flow of the electrons without suffering any resistance. On the other hand, the *thermal* vibrations of the atoms, which are added when we start to heat up the metal, will at some temperature become strong enough to cause scattering of the electrons, and so produce electrical resistance once more.

The birth of this general sort of idea was due essentially to two brilliant physicists, Herbert Fröhlich and John Bardeen. The first thing that we have to ask of this or any other new idea is whether it will work out quantitatively, and whether or not it predicts correctly the various properties that can be observed, in this case those of superconductivity. When Fröhlich first put forward his ideas, he pointed out two consequences of his theory which still seem, very roughly speaking, to be correct. First, the zero-point vibrations of the atoms will affect the behavior of the conduction electrons strongly and lead to superconductivity only if they can interact with the electrons with sufficient vigor. Fröhlich suggested that the strength of this interaction, or *coupling,* as it is called, would be somewhat the same as the strength of interaction between the electrons and the *thermal* vibrations of the atoms. Now the ordinary electrical resistance of a metal at normal temperatures depends on how strongly the electrons are being scattered by the thermal vibrations of the atoms, and naturally the stronger the interaction is between the electrons and the thermal vibrations, the greater will be the ordinary electrical resistance. Thus Fröhlich's theory suggested that one should expect to find superconductivity at very low temperatures only in those metals which actually had quite a high electrical resistance at normal temperatures—that is to say, in those metals where the coupling, or interaction, between the thermal vibrations and the electrons was quite large.

On the whole this prediction seems quite well fulfilled. We said earlier that none of the group IA or IB metals was found to be a superconductor, and yet all these metals (copper, silver, gold, sodium, potassium, etc.) are pretty good conductors at normal temperatures. In earlier years this situation often seemed rather surprising; since these metals are very good conductors at normal temperatures, one might have expected that they would be good candidates for becoming *super*conductors at very low temperatures.[8] But now one sees that this is just the opposite to what is suggested theoretically because in a good conductor the interaction between the thermal vibrations of the atoms and the conduction electrons is rather small. And according to Fröhlich we should then expect that the interaction between zero-point vibrations and the electrons will also be rather small, and con-

[8] This is sometimes the most exciting feature of theories in science when they clearly predict that something should happen which at first sight seems almost ridiculous. The great theoretical physicist Wolfgang Pauli, who died in 1958, once said of a new theory about a fundamental subject that it was crazy—but not crazy enough!

sequently not able to "sweep" the electrons along strongly enough to produce superconductivity.

The second prediction of the theory, which we have already mentioned in passing, relates to what happens in a superconductor as we increase the temperature. If we imagine starting off at absolute zero with a metal where the coupling between the electrons and zero-point vibrations is strong enough to make it a superconductor, then as we heat up the metal this superconductive coupling will tend to be broken down sooner or later by the increasing random thermal vibrations of the atoms. We would therefore expect that at some temperature or other the electrical resistance will reappear and this is, of course, just what we do find.

Finally, we note that a magnetic field exerts a force on any metal carrying an electric current; that is to say, there is interaction or coupling between a magnetic field and the conduction electrons.[9] So perhaps we might also expect that a strong enough magnetic field acting on a superconductor could interfere with the coupling of the electrons to the zero-point vibrations of the atoms; therefore, a strong enough magnetic field should also be able to annul superconductivity and restore the electrical resistance. Again this is just what we find experimentally. Indeed, on this sort of argument one would expect that any suitable combination of thermal vibrations (i.e., increasing the temperature) together with a magnetic field could also do the job of breaking down superconductivity. And that is just what we do find. For example, in

[9] This force is very familiar to everyone because it is the force that makes any electric motor go around. This force drives electric trains (real or toy ones), starts the engine in your automobile with the starter motor, and drives the furnace motor and fan motor in your house if you have that kind of central heating.

the metal lead we need a magnetic field of about 800 gauss[10] at the absolute zero of temperature in order to kill the superconductivity; at 4.2°K (boiling point of liquid helium) about 540 gauss is sufficient to do the job, while at 7°K it would need only about 40 gauss to produce electrical resistance. At about 7.2°K the thermal vibrations are strong enough by themselves, and above that temperature the resistance of lead behaves quite normally. (See Fig. 11.)

In the past few years a great deal more theoretical work has been done on the problem, particularly by Bardeen and his colleagues,* and altogether we can probably say that physicists now have a reasonably sound understanding of superconductivity, although many particular aspects still await investigation. For example, while Fröhlich's ideas gave us a broad picture of why some groups of metals might be superconductors but not others, I think it would be rash to say that we could predict with certainty whether any *particular* compound or alloy we might make would become a superconductor. This leads us back to some of the practical applications of superconductivity. If we are to use superconductors more widely, it would be very helpful to find substances that would stay superconductors at more easily attainable temperatures. I mentioned earlier that columbium (or niobium) is the element that stays superconducting to the highest temperature—but this temperature is only about 9° above the absolute zero (i.e., about −264°C!). By making compounds we can use superconductors up to appreciably higher temperatures. The highest that I know of today is a compound of

[10] I.e., about 1500 times the earth's magnetic field.

* The most recent theoretical developments are quite detailed and can account remarkably well for many properties of superconductors. I hope the theoreticians will forgive my very rough and perhaps superficial account of the problems.

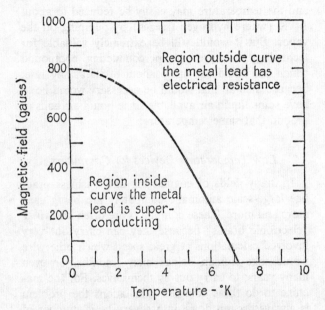

FIG. 11. *The metal lead becomes superconductive on cooling below about 7.2°K. At still lower temperatures we can transform it back to a normal conductor with a sufficiently strong magnetic field.*

niobium and tin (Nb_3Sn), which remains superconducting to about 18°K. To make use of the superconducting properties of this compound we would not need liquid helium. Liquid hydrogen would do; it boils under one atmosphere pressure at about 20°K, and the temperature may easily be reduced to about 14°K (where hydrogen freezes) by pumping off the vapor. But it would still be extremely valuable for technology to have a superconducting compound which one could use up to about 80°K at any rate, because then all that would be necessary would be to have some liquid air available since liquid air boils at around that same temperature.

Low Temperature Devices for Computers

In many fields of engineering and business practice large-scale automatic computers are being used more and more. These computers are often known as "electronic brains" because they can carry out very involved calculations at great speed which otherwise would take human beings many months, or even many years, to carry out by themselves. For the machine to do these complex calculations the problem is always broken down into a very large number of elementary steps of addition or multiplication. For example, you are asked to divide 1698 by 24. Either you could do this by the standard method of long division that one learns in school, or you might first start dividing 1698 by 2, giving 849; dividing again by 2, giving 424.5; again dividing by 2 giving 212.25; and finally dividing by 3, giving 70.75 for the final answer. Or, if you had to multiply 1698 by 24, you could do it in the same sort of stages; i.e., $2 \times 1698 = 3396$; $2 \times 3396 = 6792$; $2 \times 6792 = 13,584$; and finally, $3 \times 13,584 = 40,752$. This way of working might seem rather pedestrian and childish to us at first sight, but if one can do each individual step rapidly enough, then it may be faster than by long division or long multiplication. The vital point is that a machine may be able to do one of these simple steps of multiplication or division in about 10^{-6} of a second (1 microsecond). So even a pretty complicated calculation, which might need a thousand of these individual steps, could then be done in a thousandth of a second all told, which is, of course, far faster than any human being could do it.

Mind you, the human being remains rather essential! As things stand today, he still has to "program," or "teach," the machine how to do the calculation, and moreover decide what calculation to do. And I doubt whether any of these automatic computers is yet in a position to make any significantly *new* contributions to physical science, although they have been used to compose some quite acceptable types of musical melody and harmony—but doubtless what is "acceptable" will be a very individual matter!

An automatic telephone system could be thought of as a rather limited type of computing machine. When we operate the dial, we are feeding into the machine appropriate electric signals which will then operate various switches in turn, and these switches ultimately connect our telephone with other extensions that we want out of hundreds, or thousands, of telephone lines in a city. Moreover, such a telephone system might easily be fitted up with a "memory" device. If the line or group of lines that we want are occupied just now, the switching system would remain in a certain state (i.e., keep its "memory" of the call we want), and when the line becomes free, it would then complete the switching and so connect up our call for us. Quite generally, a giant com-

puting machine must be able to carry through a
very large number of elementary switching operations (something like an automatic telephone system)
at great speed, and can store in its memory a large
number of bits of data that may be needed again at
a later stage in the calculation. This is something like
the memory system that I suggested for an automatic
telephone system which would hold needed information until the appropriate line became free for our
call. Broadly speaking, there is thus a great demand
for very small, compact, units to use for switching
or storage ("memory") purposes. These units must
operate at extremely high speed, and moreover each
switching or storage element must consume very little power. This last demand should be obvious if we
think of an automatic computer with perhaps a million operating elements in all. If each element (a
switch or memory unit) required only 10 watts on
the average to keep it operating (and this is only the
power used in a very small electric light bulb), it
would need 10 megawatts of power altogether or, in
other words, about 13,000 horsepower, to keep such
a computer working. When you realize that this
power would be enough to supply a small town of
some thousand houses, you will realize how important it is to search for individual computer units that
require very little power. It may also help to realize
what is wanted if I mention that the *human* brain
has at least 10,000 million (10^{10}) switching elements
(and perhaps very considerably more), while at the
same time the whole power consumption of the human body, even when we are sitting down and thinking as hard as we can, is only about 60 watts, or
enough to light one ordinary light bulb!

Many different devices have been used, and are
being tried, to provide these switching and memory

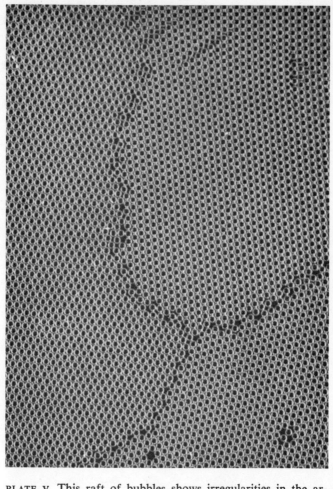

PLATE V. This raft of bubbles shows irregularities in the arrangement which are rather similar to the irregularities produced by dislocations and grain boundaries in a metal crystal. This "bubble raft" model was developed by Sir Lawrence Bragg and Dr. J. F. Nye at the Cavendish Laboratory in Cambridge. It has proved most valuable in understanding the structure and mechanical properties of metals.

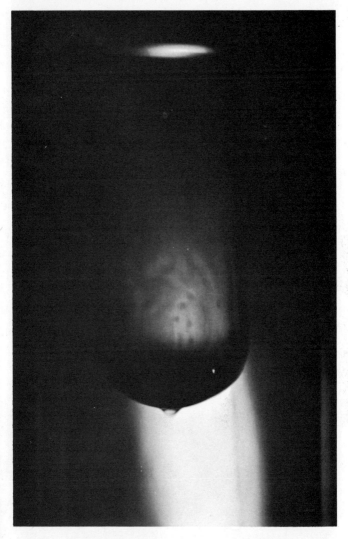

PLATE VI. A photograph of "superfluid" liquid helium dripping off the end of a beaker inside an apparatus designed for very low temperature experiments. (Dr. Howard O. McMahon of Arthur D. Little Inc. very kindly provided this photograph.)

PLATE VII. With a boiling point of −196 C. (−320 F.), liquid nitrogen will boil off when sitting on a cake of dry ice. *Courtesy LINDE COMPANY, Division of Union Carbide Corporation.*

devices for "electronic brains," and tiny superconducting switches are certainly candidates for the job.
For example, we saw earlier that a superconducting
wire can be "switched off" (i.e., the electrical resistance can be made to reappear) by applying a suitable magnetic field to the superconductor. One clever
idea from which other devices have been developed
is to use *another* superconducting wire close by,
which passes a current to provide this magnetic field
for switching. An early device of this type, known as
a cryotron,[11] was invented by Dr. D. A. Buck[12] of
the Massachusetts Institute of Technology. Such superconducting devices can be made extremely small
by using very fine wires or even very thin evaporated
films of metals. In principle it should be possible to
keep the power consumption very low indeed because, as you remember, the whole point is that an
electric current flowing in a superconductor does not
meet with any resistance at all, and so does not consume any power.

Superconducting devices have been used also in
laboratories for a number of years in making very
sensitive measurements, and there seems little doubt
that within the next few years more and more will be
found in both scientific work and industrial applications.

[11] The prefix *cry* is from a Greek word meaning "frost"
and hence something cold; the idea behind the word *cryotron*
is of course that one has to have very low temperatures in
order to use a superconductor. Some people refer to the
whole science of using low temperatures as "cryogenics," and
it is certainly quite common to call a very low temperature
apparatus a "cryostat."

[12] I am sad to hear that Dr. Buck has since died; at a recent scientific meeting, a special D. A. Buck Memorial Ses-
sion was held on superconductive devices.

CHAPTER 4

HELIUM IS INTERESTING STUFF

In earlier chapters I have tried to show why the physicist must turn to liquid helium to enable him to reach very low temperatures, but his interest in helium does not end there. It is also true that liquid helium itself provides a fascinating subject for study at these very low temperatures. Oddly enough, you might say the same thing about water. Water is a most useful substance for providing both heating and cooling. We use hot water in radiators (and even hot water bottles) to keep us warm, and there is nothing more welcome than ice cubes from the refrigerator to keep us cool in summer. But at the same time water has many fascinating properties of its own that have attracted the chemist and physicist for many years. For example, the ability of water to store up heat is almost unique, and makes it so useful in a hot water bottle. If you filled the hot water bottle with some other liquid at the same temperature, you would almost certainly find that it would cool down much more rapidly than when it is filled with hot water. Secondly, most substances get heavier when they freeze, and this is not unexpected for we would tend to predict that atoms would come closer together in a solid than in the liquid. But water does just the opposite; ice is *lighter* than water, which is precisely why icebergs float in the ocean and, moreover, why ponds and rivers form ice on the top in winter, rather than freezing from the bottom up—a happy circumstance, I believe, for the fish.

Now to see why the behavior of liquid helium is peculiar, we must first ask what physics has to say about the behavior of *any* substance. The first thing we know with certainty is that atoms of any given kind always attract one another. This force of attraction can vary a great deal from one kind of atom to another, but it always appears to be sure that any two sulphur atoms, for example, will attract one another; any two hydrogen atoms, any two iron atoms, or any two chlorine atoms will always attract one another. If there were nothing else that controlled the behavior of atoms, then presumably a bunch of sulphur atoms, or a bunch of sodium atoms, when once they had the chance, would simply stick tightly together. So they would form either solid sulphur, or solid sodium as the case may be, and that would be that.

But we have also learned from the study of physical science that what might be called a universal disruptive force is at work all the time; this force is the heat in a body at a given temperature. At the temperature we live at, which is about 300 degrees above the absolute zero, the thermal vibrations of the atoms due to heat are not nearly strong enough to break down the forces of attraction between the sodium or sulphur atoms. And so in fact both sodium and sulphur are solid at room temperature. On the other hand, the forces of attraction between such atoms as helium, argon, or neon are very much weaker than they are between sodium or sulphur atoms. The thermal energy available at room temperature is much stronger than that of the natural attraction between helium or argon atoms; any time two of these atoms do come near one another they do not stick together but quickly fly apart. So at room temperature helium and argon are gases, not solids. But it is true nonetheless that two helium atoms always attract one another to some extent (likewise two argon atoms, or two neon atoms); it just means that for them the forces of attraction are much weaker than they are between two sodium atoms, or between two sulphur atoms. Now it is a fascinating question to ask *why* it is that one particular kind of atom has much stronger interatomic forces than some other kind of atom. This really is a great deal of what the whole business of chemistry is about. The detailed explanation lies in a very fundamental part of physical science and has brought physics and chemistry very close together, but unfortunately we cannot go into this question deeply here.

But, back to our story about helium atoms. When we reduce the temperature of a body, what we actually do is cut down the amount of the random thermal energy the atoms have, giving the atoms a better chance to "stick" together. If that were the whole story, then *every* kind of atom should ultimately stick to its neighbors when we give it the chance by reducing the temperature far enough. Of course, it might mean that we would need a *very* low temperature for some atoms to allow them to adhere to one another, if the forces of attraction are very weak, but it should happen sooner or later. As you lowered the temperature far enough, ultimately every substance that was originally a gas, where the atoms were flying about every-which-way and had no chance to stick together, should normally first become a liquid.[1] In

---

[1] This is certainly the usual behavior, but once again the pressure that we apply plays some part in determining

a liquid the atoms adhere together to some extent, but not quite rigidly—they are still able to move about fairly easily among one another. But as you reduced the temperature still further, every substance should finally solidify, in which case the atoms would have so little random thermal motion that the forces of attraction to one another would arrange the atoms into quite regular patterns. Such a pattern is just what a crystalline solid is.

Forces between Atoms

This is certainly the universal picture that one would have expected theoretically, and indeed was found experimentally, until about fifty years ago when Kamerlingh Onnes first set about trying to liquefy the last element that then remained a gas at very low temperatures—namely, helium. The specific reason why helium was the last element to be attacked by low temperature physicists is that it is the lightest member of the family known as the *inert* atoms. We know that the electrons whizzing around in an atom are responsible for the attraction between the atoms, and in the group of elements helium, neon, argon, krypton, and xenon these electrons form in each element what we could call a particularly compact, "happy" family. The families of electrons in atoms are specially stable when they compose certain even-

---

whether a substance becomes a liquid or a solid first on cooling. One well-known example of the latter behavior is carbon dioxide (CO_2). If you cool it under one atmosphere pressure, it changes directly from a gas to a solid (i.e., without becoming a liquid in between) at $-78°C$. Solid carbon dioxide is known colloquially as "dry ice" (although it is far colder than ordinary ice) because as it warms up, it turns into gas and no liquid is formed. It never becomes "wet" and therefore is very convenient for some forms of refrigeration.

numbered groups—namely, 2 (as in helium); 10 (neon); 18 (argon); 36 (krypton); 54 (xenon). In these atoms the electrons are so well "mated" in pairs together that as a family they show very little interest in joining up with any other electrons. Consequently, such atoms show very little attraction for any other atom, although, as I said earlier, there is always some little attraction to be found. The fewer number of electrons there are, the less there will be any attraction at all. So helium, as the lightest atom of this group, with the fewest electrons (only 2), provides only a very modest attractive force to any other helium atom. What attraction exists between such atoms comes about because the atoms as a whole tend, very roughly speaking, to vibrate electrically in sympathy with one another, and it is this *sympathetic electrical vibration* that ultimately brings about the attraction. To sum up, helium is the lightest atom of this inert family of atoms, has the fewest electrons, and the "sympathetic vibrations" are the weakest of all. Helium has only two electrons to make up the atom; since these electrons form a very well-matched pair, helium shows the least attraction of *any* atom for its fellows.

Kamerlingh Onnes himself had made a rough estimate from his earlier experiments on helium *gas,* that he would somehow need to reduce the temperature to about 5° above the absolute zero before the thermal motion would be small enough to allow helium atoms to come together to form a liquid. When the crucial experiment was made, sure enough, liquid helium *did* finally form at about 4.2°K. So far as that went, the cooling went according to plan, and helium liquefied more or less as expected theoretically. But even on that first day of experiments in the University of Leiden in 1908 the investigators did not stop there. They put a vacuum pump on to the liquid helium, and the pumping then had the effect, by drawing off the vapor, of cooling the liquid helium still further. We saw in Chapter 2 that this is a powerful means of cooling down a liquid, because the more energetic atoms are those that get up into the vapor, and if one removes them continually with a vacuum pump, the liquid is left with more and more sluggish atoms and naturally becomes colder. In those very first experiments they cooled down liquid helium to about 2° above the absolute zero, expecting the liquid to freeze. But in fact it did not freeze. This result was surprising, because the temperature had been reduced to at least *half* what it was when helium first formed a liquid at one atmosphere pressure, and yet there was no sign of it freezing. Hydrogen becomes liquid at one atmosphere pressure around 20°K, and if you cool it down by putting a vacuum pump on it, it will freeze at about 14°K. That is to say, the freezing point is about two-thirds of the boiling point. Water is not too much different; the freezing point is at 273°K (0°C) and the boiling point at 373°K (100°C), the ratio here being about three-quarters. But now you see that in liquid helium we have reduced the temperature to less than half the boiling-point temperature, and yet the helium still has remained liquid.

Zero-Point Energy

In many later experiments liquid helium was cooled much further with more and more powerful vacuum pumps. Indeed, the temperature of liquid helium has been lowered in this way to less than one degree above the absolute zero (about 0.8°K), but *still* it shows no sign of freezing. We have every reason to believe today that no matter how far you would cool liquid helium, it would never by itself become solid. That is not to say you cannot *make* it solid. You can if you apply enough pressure from outside; it takes about 30 atmospheres pressure at 1°K to do the trick. But this need to apply pressure from outside to make helium freeze suggests that perhaps there is some factor missing in the picture of the behavior of atoms that we have outlined. It seems to suggest that there must be some further disruptive "force" that tends to prevent the helium atoms' coming together tightly enough to form a solid, and we overcome this "force" by applying pressure from outside. This new "force" preventing freezing in helium cannot be the heat energy because we have now reduced the temperature in liquid helium drastically below the boiling point and have come rather close to the absolute zero, and yet something is still stopping the helium atoms from crystallizing together.

This force, which persists right down to the absolute zero of temperature, turns out to be the zero-point energy, which we met before when discussing metals in Chapter 3, and in particular the problem of superconductivity. Even at the lowest temperatures, when we visualize helium as made up of a collection of atoms, we must also think of the atoms as jiggling around, or vibrating, quite strongly, just because they are so very light. If an atom is one of the heavier ones, then its zero-point energy will not disturb appreciably its position at low temperatures; so if we remove the thermal energy by cooling, the attractive forces between the atoms cause the substance to freeze, as we well know. On the other hand, because helium atoms are so light, we must think of them as being jiggled around rather violently by the zero-point energy. This is rather like saying that if you manage to hit a wasp, then the energy of the slap you gave it will knock the wasp for a four-bagger.[2] On the other hand, the same slap given to an elephant would not disturb the elephant very much. So you must think of helium atoms as little wasps being slapped around by the zero-point energy and the heavier atoms as heavy elephants who all but ignore its effects. Thus, the combination of the very weak forces of attraction between helium atoms, together with their extreme sensitivity to the zero-point energy, leads to a unique property: unless we apply additional forces from outside (i.e., high pressures), helium remains liquid down to the very lowest temperatures.

Superfluids

But there is more to the story. When we start to cool down liquid helium from its boiling point at $4.2°K$, it behaves more or less as a normal, but very light, liquid (its density is only about one-tenth that of water); but as we cool it below about $2.2°K$, something very remarkable occurs. One finds that the liquid then will conduct heat with great efficiency (much better than many metals), and also that in certain circumstances it seems to flow from place to place very freely without needing any "push" to keep it moving. Normally, if you try to make a liquid go through a narrow tube (often called a capillary tube), you have to exert some pressure to keep it going, and this pressure increases rapidly the narrower the tube is made. We say that we are having to overcome the viscosity, or friction, or "stickiness" of the liquid. What we are actually doing on a microscopic scale

[2] Canadian and English readers, who are familiar with cricket, perhaps would prefer to say that we would hit a wasp "for six."

is to heat up the liquid a bit; ultimately much of the work that we do in pushing liquid through a fine tube ends up as random energy of the individual atoms, and this energy is just heat. But one finds that liquid helium below about 2°K will flow readily through very fine capillary tubes and over surfaces without needing any force to push it at all. In this state the liquid helium is called "superfluid."[3] This leads to the very odd situation that if you fill up a small beaker or jar with liquid helium inside an apparatus below 2.2°K, and then lift the jar out of the "superfluid" helium in the apparatus, the liquid will spontaneously climb out of the small jar in a fine invisible film over its surface, and drop off into the surrounding liquid without your doing anything about it—or rather, perhaps, in spite of anything you might do about it! This behavior is sketched in Fig. 12, and Plate VI shows a photograph of an actual experiment.

The properties of liquid helium change so dramatically below 2.2°K that it is known as liquid helium I above 2.2°K, and liquid helium II below this temperature. The change-over point, which is quite sharp and occurs more exactly at 2.19°K, is known technically as the *lambda point*.[4] Now what ideas can we have of this very remarkable liquid helium II, which shows enormous heat conductivity and no "stickiness" under certain conditions? Like supercon-

[3] The behavior of the liquid helium below 2°K in flowing freely through fine tubes and over surfaces reminds us a bit of the free flow of electrons in those metals that become superconductors at low temperatures. This interesting analogy was pointed out some years ago by Dr. F. London and Dr. K. Mendelssohn, and the similarity in behavior is still of considerable interest.

[4] This name arises because when you plot on a graph how certain properties of liquid helium change with temperature, the graph shows a sharp peak at 2.19°K, and this peak looks something like the Greek letter lambda (λ, Λ).

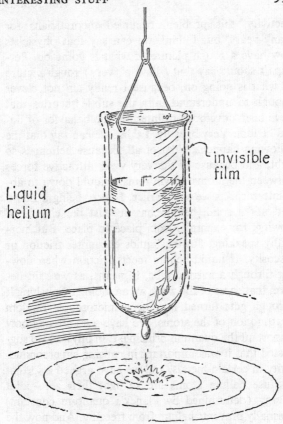

Liquid helium bath

FIG. 12. *If a beaker of liquid helium, which is cooled below 2.19°K, is lifted out from the liquid, then it will empty itself by a fine invisible film which covers the whole beaker. Drops will form steadily on the outside of the beaker at the bottom and from there drain back continuously into the main bath of the liquid helium. (These sketches are suggested by a paper by Drs. J. G. Daunt and K. Mendelssohn who did pioneer work at the Clarendon Laboratory, Oxford University, in this field just before the last war.)*

ductivity, this problem occupied theoreticians for
many years, but I think we can say that physicists
now have a rough picture of what is going on. Perhaps I should say that *I* have a (very) rough picture
of what is going on, because I really am not clever
enough to understand fully the subtle theories that
have been developed to interpret the behavior of liquid helium. Very broadly, I think we can say that the
following happens. First of all, because helium is so
light, and because of the very weak attractive forces
between the atoms, it will remain liquid down to absolute zero, as we saw earlier. Hence, being a liquid
and not a solid, helium has at least the chance of
flowing, for example, from place to place. But, normally speaking, flowing liquids encounter friction or
viscosity. If liquid helium meets friction when flowing through a narrow tube, it means, as we said before, that some of the work we are doing by pushing it
through gets turned into some microscopic random
heat motion of the atoms. We have seen already how
important the quantum principle is in physics; we suggested that it was important in causing superconductivity in certain metals, and we have argued also that
because helium atoms are so light their zero-point
energy (determined by Planck's quantum constant)
normally prevents helium from freezing. And now the
quantum principle appears to be important yet again
in helping us to understand the superfluid behavior of
liquid helium. If the liquid has to encounter viscosity
or friction, then a microscopic heat motion has to be
generated in that liquid, and it seems from the quantum principle that we can only generate the necessary
microscopic motion of the atoms in little energy-
bundles of a minimum amount. In liquids at normal
temperatures, where quite a lot of thermal energy is
knocking about, this presents no difficulty because

these bundles, or quanta, are so tiny. However, at very low temperatures, where there is very little thermal energy, it may be difficult to generate these particular bundles of energy and so to produce the right kind of random motion of the helium atoms to absorb the viscous or frictional energy. In other words, at very low temperatures it may be impossible to produce the right kind of atomic motion in liquid helium necessary for friction, and if that is so, there just cannot be any friction.

So, to sum up, we can say in broad terms that helium itself behaves in a very remarkable way at very low temperatures because it is a very light atom and so is very sensitive to the effects of the so-called zero-point energy. Secondly, because it is a small and inert atom, it has only very weak interaction forces with its neighbors, and this property, coupled with the zero-point motion, keeps helium a liquid down to the very lowest temperatures. Thirdly, because helium is a liquid at very low temperatures, *other* consequences of the quantum effects militate against viscosity or friction. Putting these three facts together, perhaps we can see how it is that helium behaves at low temperatures in this paradoxical manner.

While everything else is frozen up solid, helium can remain a liquid, and not only that, but a liquid which in certain circumstances can flow about with no resistance whatever to its movement. Where does this lead us then? First, the job of understanding how liquid helium can behave so remarkably helps physicists to understand more thoroughly the behavior of more humdrum liquids in general. Perhaps this is a bit like saying that if you can understand why the genius or madman behaves as he does, you may well end up by understanding why the average man in the street behaves as *he* does. Secondly, to be able to

make experiments in a liquid which has very unusual
properties can help in the exploration of other fields
of science. In hydrodynamics or aerodynamics one
has to study the flow of fluids or gases over and
around surfaces, which might be the hulls of ships or
the wings of aircraft, and determine what forces are
exerted on the hulls or the wings. Often the predictions of theory will be tested in a wind tunnel or in
a water tank with scaled-down models of the aircraft
or vessel concerned. But in some special cases it might
well happen that the study of a model moving in an
"ultracold, superfluid" bath of liquid helium might
afford a more direct test of some extreme aspects of
aerodynamical theory than could be obtained otherwise. And finally, the direct practical possibilities of
using a fluid which can sometimes show apparently
frictionless behavior will be, I am sure, a natural challenge to the engineer. Thus liquid helium, although
it can never exist except under the most "abnormal"
surroundings, can play a most important role in both
fundamental science and engineering.

But this is not the whole story of liquid helium.
Perhaps there never is a whole story, in any part of
physical research. In some ways perhaps the beauty
of research in science is that when one problem has
been solved, you can begin to tackle the next one,
which sometimes has only shown itself to be a problem precisely because you have answered the previous
question. But, back to the grindstone.

The Behavior of Light Helium

It happens that helium atoms having different
masses exist. Each helium atom has a nucleus, where
practically all the mass resides, and each helium nucleus has always got two protons in it. These two

protons together carry two positive electric charges, which in turn hold in orbit the two electrons that continually whizz around outside the nucleus and cause the atom to be specifically a helium atom. However, if the two protons were the entire nucleus, they would be liable to blow one another apart. We need something else to "glue" the protons together. Two neutrons do this gluing very efficiently. With them we have a common or garden variety of helium atom whose mass is about 4 units (protons and neutrons all weigh about the same). This is the kind of helium atom I have been talking about so far in this chapter. But you can also glue two protons together with only one neutron to make the nucleus of a helium atom, although this is a less efficient kind of gluing, and so leads to a much less common type of helium atom. In this case we have a helium atom which weighs a lot less, only 3 mass units (2 protons plus 1 neutron) instead of 4, and this is the helium denoted by the symbol He^3.

Just because He^3 atoms are considerably lighter than the commoner He^4 type, we would expect that the influence of the zero-point energy would be even more marked. This is true. We have seen already in Chapter 2 that He^3 boils at an even lower temperature (about $3°K$) than the heavier He^4 does. But, on the other hand, when we cool down liquid He^3, it does *not* go through this sudden change (we called it the lambda point) which liquid He^4 goes through when it becomes superfluid and also shows very high heat conductivity. Liquid He^3 certainly remains a liquid down to the very lowest temperatures, but some of the quantum effects are relatively different in the lighter liquid than in the heavier one. I think I am right in saying that no one knows for *sure* today precisely why the two types of liquid helium show this different behavior, He^4 becoming superfluid while He^3 does not. Many theorists feel that it must be due ultimately to matters of symmetry. When one takes fuller account of these quantum effects we have mentioned in what is called quantum mechanics, one finds that questions of symmetry become extremely important in discussions of the behavior of fundamental particles, such as electrons, protons, neutrons, and so on.[5] Now the heavier helium atom (He^4) has altogether 6 fundamental particles (2 protons and 2 neutrons in the nucleus, and 2 electrons circling about); on the other hand, an He^3 atom is made up of only 5 particles (2 protons and 1 neutron in the nucleus, and 2 electrons outside). In the first atom we have an *even* number of particles altogether, and in the second an *odd* number of particles. And this discrepancy can make a vital difference in the symmetry effects involved in quantum mechanics, in something like the way a square, which is a four-sided figure, is fundamentally different from a triangle, which is a three-sided figure.

If we want to go further in trying to understand the behavior of liquid helium, we really have to make a fresh start and try to tackle the problem fundamentally, but even today this is proving very difficult for the cleverest theorists, so I think without any shame *we* can leave our discussion of the question here!

[5] In recent years the problem of symmetry in nuclear reactions particularly, cropped up most strikingly in discussions of what is called *parity*. Physicists had generally believed that certain symmetry properties must always be maintained in nuclear reactions, but two young American physicists, Doctors C. N. Yang and T. D. Lee, showed that this was not always true, and that sometimes conservation of parity was violated in certain nuclear reactions. For this discovery they received the 1957 Nobel Prize in Physics.

CHAPTER 5

HOW OTHER SCIENCES MAKE USE OF LOW TEMPERATURE PHYSICS

Thus far we have talked mainly about the sort of things at low temperatures that have been discussed and studied by the particular group of people usually known as "low temperature physicists." And when I say "particular group," that is just what I do mean. Until fairly recently very low temperature physics was, on the whole, a most specialized branch of science. Those studying and working in it often felt that they belonged to quite a select club, and it is still true that every two years there is an international conference devoted to low temperatures. In 1958 it was held in Leiden, where helium was first liquefied fifty years earlier, and in 1960 it was held in Toronto, Canada, at the MacLennan Laboratories.[1] Before the 1939–1945 war there were very few laboratories in the world specializing in this kind of work, and even such countries as Germany, Russia, and Great Britain had only one or two. Very shortly after the war Sir Francis Simon organized a small and quite informal conference to discuss problems of low temperature physics at Oxford, and the guests numbered perhaps two or three dozen. Nowadays many hun-

[1] Sir John Cunningham MacLennan, F.R.S. (1867–1935), was responsible for the first liquefaction of helium in Canada around 1922, and built up a flourishing laboratory at the University of Toronto specializing in low temperature physics.

dreds of scientists take part in these International
Low Temperature Conferences; one meets chemists,
mechanical engineers, and all kinds of physicists who
use very low temperatures for their work. It is still
true that there is a group of physicists who specialize
in the problems of *extreme* low temperatures, and to
whom we often look for guidance in tackling the
problems at the frontiers. But today liquid helium is
available for use in many laboratories in the world;
even in Canada I can think of eight laboratories immediately, and there may well be twice as many,
where liquid helium is used regularly.

Chemistry and Low Temperatures

We can hark back to our introduction to low temperatures to see just why liquid helium has become
a very valuable tool for use in many branches of science. One might say that any problem in physical
science almost always ends up by asking what happens to the energy in a system. If a chemist is studying
a chemical reaction, he wants to know how the energy is released when he brings together two substances which can interact with one another, and how
much energy release occurs in the reaction. When a
mechanical engineer is puzzled why some metals
slowly stretch when they are kept under tension for
a long period, he will have to find out how the energy
is provided to move the atoms about in the metal,
and so on. Now as we go to lower and lower temperatures, we have seen that the "blurring" effect of
the everlasting random thermal energy of the atoms
and molecules is reduced enormously, and so we can
find out in detail how energy changes occur which
otherwise we could not observe. Thus low tempera-

tures offer a means for studying the detailed structure of energy changes in many different applications.

A very important concept the chemists have used to explain why certain chemical reactions occur is that of "free radicals." When two substances were brought together and joined in a chemical reaction to produce two other substances, chemists often found it necessary to suppose that "on the way" some very short-lived molecular fragments were formed which then recombined quickly to produce the final state of the reaction. Naturally the chemists, to get on further with their ideas, would like to be able to examine in more detail at leisure the behavior of these supposed "free radicals." However, the trouble is generally that the free radicals live such short lives; when the reaction is happening, the random thermal motion of the atoms is so strong that these fragments combine to form new compounds almost as soon as they themselves are formed. The shortness of the time intervals naturally makes it exceedingly difficult for the chemist to study these free radicals as fully as he might like to.

Perhaps it is somewhat like planting grass seeds in the ground. We start off with grass seeds, dull lifeless looking things which we place in the ground to begin the "reaction," so to speak. Then, perhaps almost overnight, we find that grass shoots are appearing above ground. We know that there must be *something* going on in between, but it may be very difficult to examine this something in detail because if you try to open up the ground and see what is happening, you will probably damage the grass seed so much that you won't get any grass at all! In the past the chemist has often had to ask the spectroscopist for help in "seeing" these free radicals, because the spectroscopist can make measurements of a certain kind which require only a tiny fraction of a second for a photograph to be taken through a spectroscope. If he is lucky and gets just the right conditions, he may be able to catch a signal from the free radical in passing. But the spectroscopist has got to be pretty careful to get the timing just right, and it is not unlike the difficulties of photographing a lightning flash in detail.

Physics and Engineering

On the other hand, it now turns out that if we arrange things properly, we can make some of these free radical molecular fragments condense on a very cold surface when some chemical reaction occurs. We might arrange for them to condense quickly onto the walls of a vessel full of liquid air, liquid hydrogen, or liquid helium. It may be that we can remove the disturbing thermal energy so quickly that the molecular fragments can no longer change quickly into the usual final state. So we may be able to watch what happens over quite long periods. This kind of free radical chemistry is now being studied at a number of laboratories, and looks like a very promising tool for the future.

We mentioned the business of metals "flowing" over a long period of time if we apply a certain stress to them. This is known as "creep," and it is naturally extremely important for the mechanical engineer to find out as much as possible about why, and how, this happens. In a solid piece of metal each atom is sitting in a sort of "cage." This cage is really an energy cage, which means that unless the atom is given a very large "punch" of energy it will stay in that cage, although it will vibrate around in the usual way at any particular temperature. Now as long as each atom stays in its own cage or cell, then the metal will never change its shape, or creep. Engineers and physicists have to suppose, however, that occasionally any individual atom manages to collect together (from the neighboring atoms, so to speak) just enough excess of energy to get out from its own cage, and so move a bit in the metal. It might well be that the chance of a single atom's getting enough energy is only one in a million million vibrations ($1/10^{12}$), but when one recalls that at room temperature an atom in a typical metal will vibrate around a million million times a second (10^{12}/sec), one sees that each atom on the average might then jump from its own cell to some other neighboring position once every second. Over a fair period of time the total deformation in the metal might be quite serious, because a considerable number of atoms could then have moved from place to place.

One way to study this sort of thing experimentally is to apply different forces or "loads" to the metal, and see how long it takes for a measurable amount of flow or creep to happen. And, indeed, in this way engineers and physicists have learned a good deal about the problem. Another very powerful method would be to see what happens as we cool a metal down to low temperatures. If we assume that an atom vibrates thermally about 10^{12} times a second at room temperature (say 300°K), then at 3°K, to which we can cool a metal by putting it in liquid helium, the thermal vibrations should now be about a hundred times slower—i.e., about 10^{10} times per second. If we think of the case I mentioned where an atom had one chance in 10^{12} vibrations of jumping out of its cell, we see that an atom should perhaps now take a hundred seconds or so ($10^{12}/10^{10} = 10^2$) to make a single jump when it is cooled in liquid helium. This slowing down would imply that the amount of creep in a metal cooled in liquid helium should be very much reduced because the total amount of atom movement in a given time should be much less than before. So if experiments are made on creep in metals at liquid helium temperatures, one should be able to test with some exactness whether our theories and ideas are correct.

Since the random vibrations of the atoms due to *heat* disappear as we go toward the absolute zero of temperature, we might perhaps expect that creep would also tend to stop completely if we cool a metal to extremely low temperatures, because there would be none of this thermal energy left to help an atom jump out of its cell. But then our old friend the zero-point energy has to be considered again. When we think of a solid as a collection of atoms, the quantum uncertainty principle requires us, even at absolute zero, to think of these atoms as jiggling about quite strongly, although they no longer have any *thermal* energy. So now if we apply a force to a piece of metal at the very lowest temperatures, where the thermal energy can be neglected, will the zero-point vibrations help an atom to jump out of its proper cell, and so in turn allow the metal to flow or creep? This is just the sort of question that can be of great interest to the mechanical engineer and the fundamental physicist alike. As a matter of fact, work is going on in that field here in Ottawa in the National Research Laboratories, under Dr. Z. S. Basinski.

Medical and Technical Applications

Low temperatures not only enable us to see the fine details of how the energy in matter behaves but, as we saw when discussing free radicals and creep, the use of very low temperatures can slow up enormously the rate of chemical and physical processes going on in nature. In broad terms this appears to be true also in living systems. I believe I am right in saying that when an animal hibernates in winter and its energy consumption is cut down greatly as a result, its body temperature also goes down considerably. And when the surgeon today wishes to perform a heart operation that will take some time, he can make arrangements to cool the patient down so that the energy requirements for the patient's brain are much below the normal. It is then much safer for the surgeon to operate on the heart for some time during which the brain will be deprived of fresh blood. Presumably the various chemical reactions going on in the brain have been slowed down, and as a consequence the brain's demands on the blood for fresh oxygen have been reduced. Often the reduction in temperature for these operations is quite small, around 10° to 15°F (rather less than 10°C), although if special arrangements are made, the cooling can be carried further. With hibernating animals the temperature drop can be quite appreciable, and the animal may cool down until it is not much warmer than the freezing point of water (32°F or 0°C), but this is still a quite small *relative* drop in absolute temperature of around 10 per cent.

Recently I saw a French film which showed biologists removing the heart from an embryo chicken with such care that the heart continued beating happily. With further careful treatment the heart was ultimately cooled to the temperature of liquid air (about −190°C), where it could then be stored, one might suppose indefinitely. Later the embryo heart was warmed up again to room temperature, and was started beating once more with apparently no sign of damage from its remarkable experience.

Naturally enough, no one yet suggests that this kind of fantastic experience could be attempted today with anything as complex as a whole human being, but perhaps the day *will* come when, if you want it, you can arrange to "hibernate" for a thousand years or so in liquid air, and then be "wakened up" again to see how the world has changed in the meantime. Even Rip van Winkle, or the Sleeping Beauty, might pale in envy at this length of "sleep."

I mentioned in Chapter 3 that at low temperatures it is already possible to use superconducting circuits as economical and compact devices for various kinds of measurements. Quite generally, low temperatures offer a tool for making very accurate measurements in many branches of physical science. In the past if we had to measure very small voltages, we usually set to work using electronic tubes as amplifiers to detect these voltages. In a thermionic vacuum tube a stream of electrons is boiled off from a hot cathode, and by controlling this stream of electrons by applying voltages to other parts of the tube (electrodes), we can obtain a very sensitive control of the electron current, and in this way can ultimately measure very small amounts of power. Let us assume that we have an electronic tube where the electrons are boiled off an oxide coated cathode at about 1000°K (this is quite a normal figure), and also that we can afford only one second in which to make each measurement. In that case the *minimum* power that we can distinguish or observe will be determined by the average heat energy of the electrons divided by the time available for the measurement. The average thermal energy of the electrons is proportional to the absolute temperature, T, and hence the minimum power, W, we can observe is roughly given by $W = \frac{kT}{t}$. The constant, k, which determines the average thermal energy of the electrons, is known as Boltzmann's[2] constant and has the value 1.4×10^{-23} Joules/°K—that is, 1.4×10^{-23} watt sec/°K. Thus for $T = 1000$°K and $t = 1$ sec, we find that the minimum detectable power $W = 4 \times 10^{-20}$ watts. This corresponds to saying that the lowest voltage we can measure in a resistance of one megohm (10^6 ohms) is about $0.2\mu V$ (one-fifth of a microvolt). In other words, with such a setup the random thermal motion of electrons in the vacuum tube is sufficient to blur out any voltage across that resistance smaller than this value, and in practice it would probably be difficult to measure accurately much less than $1\mu V$.

But now suppose that we can use some *other* electronic device for our measurements (perhaps a transistor, which we hear a lot about today), such that its temperature could be held at 0.1°K. Then in principle the minimum power we could detect would be 10,000 times smaller than before—i.e., about 4×10^{-24} watts—and in terms of voltage we should now be able to detect easily 10^{-8}V ($\frac{1}{100}\mu V$) with our setup.

Temperature and the Universe

Low temperatures now are offering a great challenge to those scientists who are concerned with mak-

[2] Ludwig Boltzmann (1844–1906) was born in Vienna and studied and worked at the Universities of Vienna and Graz in Austria. Boltzmann's greatest contributions to physics were in linking together the large-scale, or thermodynamic, properties of matter with the microscopic, or atomic, behavior. The Stefan-Boltzmann Law relating the radiation from a body to its temperature, and the Maxwell-Boltzmann Law relating the speed of gas molecules to the temperature of the gas, are both very fundamental in physical science.

ing extremely sensitive measurements of all kinds. It is particularly interesting to consider what is happening in Radio Astronomy. With suitable radio antenna systems (usually called radio telescopes), it is possible to detect the electromagnetic radiation coming from some of the most distant parts in the Universe—in some cases even where it is not possible to detect the star by its *visible* light, or rather the enormous collection of stars (galaxy)[3] which is emitting the radiations, because they are so far away.

One of the most interesting problems in astronomy today is to try to understand how our universe has on the whole developed over the last few billion years. One theory says that the universe started with a "bang." Some sort of gigantic and enormously hot explosion is supposed to have occurred when our various chemical elements were first manufactured out of hydrogen, and then by the force of this explosion matter was blown into space and then as time went on formed into galaxies, stars, suns, moons, and so on. On this theory our universe is still blowing itself apart all the time, and getting steadily older with the passing years. There is, however, another theory which says that, on the average, our universe never changes very much over-all as time goes on. Suns, stars, and galaxies will disappear from our view, but new ones are being born all the time in such a way

---

[3] It is now known that the Universe is made up of enormous collections of stars, each of which may contain thousands of millions of individual stars, of which our sun is but one member. The word *galaxy* (from the Greek word for milk) referred originally to the Milky Way, which we can see on a dark night if city lights don't obscure it. This Milky Way is actually the collection of stars, seen "end on," to which our solar system belongs. It forms a rather narrow band of light in the sky because our galaxy is in the form of a relatively thin (but enormous) disc of stars.

that the average outlook from any place in the universe stays much the same.

How can we test such theories, and which is to be believed? If we can examine stars or galaxies very far away from us, we shall see these galaxies, not as they are now, but as they were perhaps two or three billion (10^9) years ago. On the first theory of the universe I mentioned, we should therefore see them as very "young" galaxies, much as we might examine a snapshot taken sixty years ago of a young man now grown very old. On the second theory, however, there should be no particular difference on the average between the appearance of those distant regions of the universe seen as they were a few billion years ago, and those which we examine at much closer range, precisely because on the second theory (the so-called "steady state" theory) the universe is much the same from place to place and does not alter on the average as time goes on.

It is clearly vital in these problems to be able to get information about the stars and galaxies that are as far away from us as possible, and radio astronomy already has proved a very powerful tool in detecting some of these very distant stellar bodies. The final limitation on making this kind of measurement depends upon being able to detect with accuracy extremely small amounts of radio power received on the antennae from the outer reaches of space. All sorts of detecting devices are tried to find the ones able to respond to lower and lower levels of incoming power, and in turn it follows that very low temperatures are quite likely to play an important role in this work. When you consider that the center of a star may well be at a temperature between ten and a hundred million degrees, it seems to me a pretty thought that we may be detecting what is going on in that star (a hundred thousand times hotter than our world) by the minute fraction of its radiation which has taken perhaps a thousand million years to reach us, and that we are using a small device which might be working at a temperature of 0.01°K—i.e., thousands of times *colder* than the world in which we live!

Truly one can say that man, who is so much "in the middle" with his own very limited life span, the temperature range wherein he can live, and the distance he can cover by himself, has reached vastly out and beyond these limits in time, space, and temperature.

INDEX

SCIENCE STUDY SERIES